# Transactive Energy

## A Sustainable Business and Regulatory Model for Electricity

Stephen Barrager, Ph.D.
Edward Cazalet, Ph.D.

Cover image courtesy of NASA.

*First Printing, January 2016*

Library of Congress Cataloging-in-Publication Data

Names: Barrager, Stephen M., author. | Cazalet, Edward G., author.
Title: Transactive energy : a sustainable business and regulatory model for
   electricity / Stephen Barrager, Ph.D., Edward Cazalet, Ph.D.
Description: Reston : Public Utilities Reports, Inc., 2016.
Identifiers: LCCN 2015049078 (print) | LCCN 2016001300 (ebook) | ISBN
   9780910325479 (pbk.) | ISBN 9780991505203 (ebook)
Subjects: LCSH: Sustainable development. | Renewable energy sources.
Classification: LCC HC79.E5 B3677 2016 (print) | LCC HC79.E5 (ebook) | DDC
   333.79/4--dc23
LC record available at http://lccn.loc.gov/2015049078

*Printed in the United States of America*

# Contents

# Preface

*When You Come to a Fork in the Road, Take It!*
*Yogi Berra[1]*

This book is about applying fundamental business concepts to move our electric power markets to a new paradigm. The heart of the new paradigm is the use of forward and spot transactions to guide investment and operating decisions.

The current paradigm is regulated cost-of-service and centralized resource optimization. This old paradigm will gradually give way to the new model as the electric system evolves from centrally planned to a decentralized energy ecosystem.

The new business and regulatory model, Transactive Energy (TE), scales well. It can coordinate decisions across the full spectrum of size and technology. It works equally well for central power-plant planning and for smart home-appliance operation. It supports both competitive pricing and cost-of-service pricing.

The TE model embodies four big ideas:

• There are two products: energy and transport services.
• Forward transactions are used to manage risk and coordinate investment decisions.
• Spot transactions are used to coordinate operating decisions.
• All parties act autonomously.

Forward transactions for energy and transport are used in the wholesale part of electric power markets today. These transactions take the form of long-term contracts for inputs and outputs. Similarly, power-system operators use spot transactions to make adjustments between predicted and actual purchases and sales. The TE model extends forward and spot transactions beyond wholesale to all corners of the market: industry, retail distributors, businesses, and homeowners.

High technology, **Moore's Law** and the Internet have descended on the slow-moving, highly regulated electric power industry. The cost of solar panels and energy storage are dropping rapidly. We can now communicate everywhere and between everything, from central power plant dispatch to iPhone to home appliance. Fast computation and data storage are inexpensive and getting cheaper by the month.

We can delegate decision-making to microcomputers embedded in our vehicles, homes, and appliances. We don't have to figure out when to set our thermostats back or which utility tariff is best for us. In the emerging world, our microcomputer "agents" will do these things for us.

We are fortunate that the technology has arrived. It will help us reduce our dependence on oil and decrease $CO_2$ emissions.

The electric power system is evolving in response to the new technology. We are seeing several new challenges and opportunities, including the following:

• Significant amounts of energy supplies with variable outputs, e.g., **wind and solar.**
• **Decentralized Energy resources,** e.g., rooftop PV panels, cogeneration, and on-site generation.
• The need for **storage** and the availability of new storage options.
• **Microgrids**: whole pieces of the market voluntarily isolating themselves and planning their own integrated energy systems.

• More **electric vehicles**.

Our outdated command-and-control system is struggling to keep up. It is stifling innovation and slowing the needed improvements in efficiency.

This book explains the Transactive Energy (TE) business and regulatory model and how we can use it to meet the future head on. We believe that the TE model is a silver bullet. It will provide incentives for investment and efficiency that will lower costs for both producers and consumers. It is fair and transparent. The TE concept is consumer friendly and politically attractive. It will spur technical and organizational innovation across the globe.

Our aim by writing this book is to expedite TE as the normal way of doing business—globally. TE is the keystone of an efficient, fair, and transparent electric power system.

This book is for the full range of stakeholders in electric-power markets:

• Customers
• Utility executives
• Legislators
• Environmentalists
• Regulators
• Economists
• Energy business professionals
• Investors and vendors
• Systems, power, and electrical engineers
• Students
• Energy researchers

The authors, Stephen Barrager and Edward Cazalet, are pioneers in the design of new methods for electric-system planning. They both studied systems engineering and economics in the Management Science and Engineering Department at Stanford University. They have built several path-breaking companies to serve the electric power industry. You can read about their qualifications in Chapter 7 titled, "Our Basis for Writing This Book."

We believe this book will provide a focus for people who are leading the move to the TE business and regulatory model worldwide. You can follow and participate in the discussion of TE with the Transactive Energy Association *(http://www.tea-web.org)*. There you will find discussions of TE from many different perspectives. And you will find questions and answers on implementation and technical details that are beyond the scope and purpose of this book.

We are at an important turning point in history. We are at the end of an era of expanding energy use and in particular energy from fossil fuels. We have the opportunity to turn the corner faster and move to a new playing field. A playing field that is eminently more level than what we currently have.

[1] Yogi Berra, When You Come to a Fork in the Road, Take It!: Inspiration and Wisdom from One of Baseball's Greatest Heroes, Hyperion, 2002, p. 1

CHAPTER 1

# Introduction

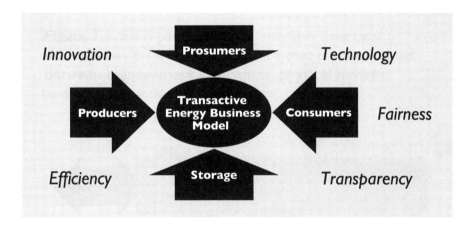

This chapter begins with a review of what is happening in the U.S. electric energy market today. Other markets around the world are experiencing similar trends. There are big changes. The changes are creating new challenges for planners and regulators.

After discussing the background we introduce the Transactive Energy (TE) business model. The TE model and rapid improvements in communication and information technology (CIT) go hand in hand. The Internet and distributed computing are making TE feasible over the entire electricity market, from single smart appliance to the largest central generation station. TE and CIT together will spur innovation and improve efficiency. This can be done in ways that are more fair and transparent than our current business model.

## Background

In 2000, the electrical system was relatively simple. It consisted of three types of customers: residential, commercial, and industrial. The residential and commercial customers were connected by a distribution system (power poles and overhead wires). The distribution systems were served by high-voltage transmission networks emanating from central power stations. Some systems incorporate pumped hydro storage (see Figure 1-1).

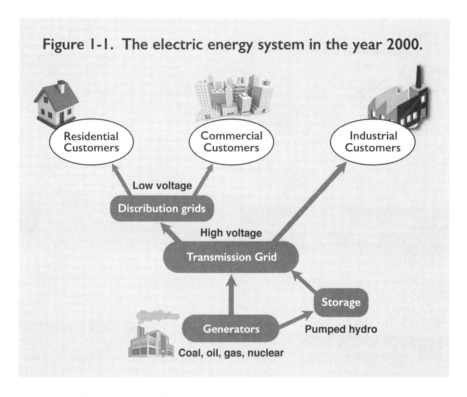

Figure 1-1. The electric energy system in the year 2000.

Ground-shaking changes have happened in the last 20 years. Social concerns about greenhouse gas emissions from power plants have caused governments to act. Society is demanding that we reduce impacts on air and water. This is forcing the early retirement of many fossil-fueled power plants in California. Concerned citizens are demanding that we increase the use of renewable, sustainable power technologies: solar, wind, and cogeneration. Entrepreneurs are eager to deploy these new technologies.

Coincident with environmental concerns we have had a lowering of natural gas production costs using **fracking** technology, especially in North America. New lower-cost gas supplies have resulted in a proliferation of decentralized gas-fueled generation facilities.

The electrical system in the year 2020 will look much different than its current configuration (see Figure 1-2). These changes to the electric market include the following:

**1) Increasing penetration of renewable generation technologies: principally wind and solar.**

**2) Increasing need for storage.** Solar and wind are variable. They are only available when the sun is shining or the wind is blowing. When the availability of wind and/or solar do not match demand, then we need a way of storing the energy so that it is not wasted. The need to capture this low-cost energy is spurring development and deployment of new technologies: batteries, thermal storage, and compressed air.

**3) Proliferating decentralized energy resources (DERs)** and "prosumers." The drive for efficiency has spurred many large customers to integrate electric power generation into their business processes. Often these businesses have excess energy to sell back into the grid. Even when large customers are energy independent, they continue to rely on grid connection for reliability. Many residential and commercial customers have installed solar panels. These customers can recover part of their investments by selling excess energy back to the grid; they are "prosumers": producers and consumers.

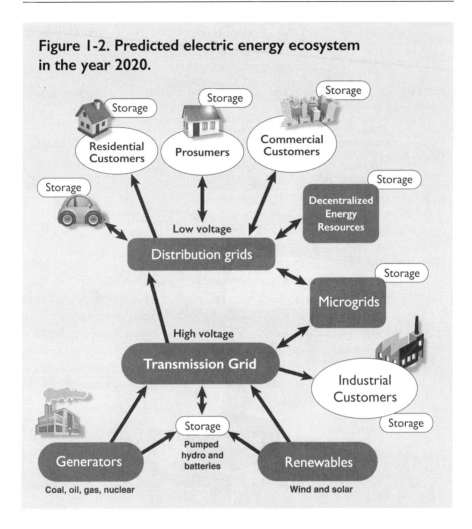

Figure 1-2. Predicted electric energy ecosystem in the year 2020.

4) **Emerging microgrids.** Whole pieces of the electric power network are peeling off from the grid. Organizations like universities or military installations are saying, "We can reduce costs and improve reliability by planning a well-integrated, stand-alone energy ecosystem." For example, the University of California, San Diego campus *(http://www.rmi.org/ucsd_microgrid)* plans and operates as an independent grid. These stand-alone "grids" capture the efficiencies of integrating and optimizing various sources and uses of energy. They can plan investments and operate their systems independent of the grid.

5) **Increasing electric vehicle sales.** Electric vehicles add a new, potentially large demand for electricity. The batteries on board the vehicles also offer an energy

storage opportunity. There is considerable flexibility on when and where the batteries are charged. With the right timing, energy can be put into the batteries and then returned to the power grid without interfering with driver needs. Vehicle storage is distributed throughout the system so it offers distribution savings and reliability benefits.

The complexity of the electric market is beginning to overwhelm regulators, planners, and operators. The large investor-owned utilities (IOUs) are struggling to meet political mandates and their commitments to customers. Municipal and other utilities face many of the same struggles although their regulatory model is different.

The struggle to integrate prosumers (mostly PV panel owners) into the grid is one indication of the challenges we are facing. California has just gone through a difficult process of reaching agreement on how to price the electricity sold back into the grid by PV panel owners.

How much should the homeowners be paid for this energy? One side says they should be paid a lot because the power comes at peak demand times and it doesn't have to be transported over expensive transmission and distribution lines. Another point of view is that money invested in transmission and distribution has to be paid by someone. If prosumers do not pay for it then the costs are unfairly dropped onto the non-prosumers.

Two months after working out a solution in California, a new problem popped up. PV panel owners started installing battery storage to back up their solar panels. They began to sell power stored in their batteries back to the utility at the Net Metering rates. The utilities want to stop this because they say it is illegal. Homeowners could simply charge their batteries with power from the grid during off peak hours and sell it back during on peak hours. This is ironic because the battery storage capability may be as valuable as the solar panels. We don't really know. What is going to happen when people start backing up their PV systems with the batteries in their electric vehicles?

These issues are very difficult for our outdated command-and-control systems to sort out. The slow pace of dealing with change is stifling innovation. Our electric utility and regulatory model is also outdated and ill equipped to deal with decentralized energy, prosumers, storage, and microgrids. TE addresses this challenge with a new model.

## The TE Business Model

We describe the TE business model in terms of how investment and operating decisions are made throughout the electric system. Investment and operating decisions are made by both producers and consumers. Producers make investments in energy generation and transport. Consumers make investments across a broad spectrum of energy producing and saving devices. Investments always entail risk. A test of a business model is how well it coordinates decisions and allows investors to manage risk.

Producers mitigate investment risk through financial devices like long-term contracts or loan guarantees. Energy project investors can limit risk by signing long-term contracts, selling portions of their project to outside investors or venture capitalists, or both.

Today many big investment decisions are made by IOUs acting under the close supervision of state and federal regulators. The IOUs have a legislatively granted franchise agreement overseen by regulators that allows them to charge customers enough to guarantee their shareholders a "fair" rate of return. IOU shareholders use this means of limiting risk. IOUs are able to borrow money at low interest rates and they pass some of this benefit on to their customers.

We have to build generating capacity without knowing exactly what demand for the plant's energy output will be, year by year, month to month, and hour to hour. Further, we don't know what future prices will be. For example, suppose we are thinking about investing in a wind farm. Our questions might include: "Will climate changes alter the wind patterns?" "At what price can I sell the energy?" "Will some new technology make our wind farm noncompetitive?" "Will transmission lines to the site be approved?" The riskiness of our investment depends on all these issues, which are uncertain at the time the decisions are made.

After energy plants are built, then we have to decide how to operate them. Operating decisions are a challenge because demand is variable and part of it is unpredictable. Figure 1-3 shows the variations in electricity demand over the course of a year for an electric utility that has its highest demand in the summer. The overall band moves up and down with the seasons. It is highest in July when air conditioning demand is the highest.

Weekend days show up as the wide bands where demand is low. You can see where demand starts to fall off early on Friday afternoon. Demand is low on Saturday and lower still on Sunday. Can you spot the holidays? Almost all the other jumping up and down is caused by daily variations in weather, especially during the Summer.

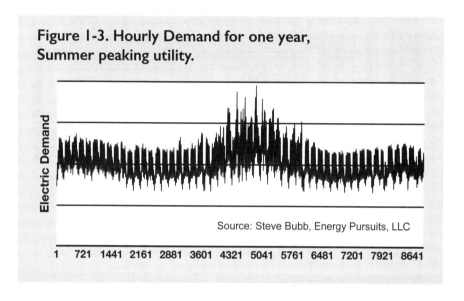

**Figure 1-3. Hourly Demand for one year, Summer peaking utility.**

In California an Independent System Operator (ISO) decides which plants are operated and when. For the large generators these decisions are mostly driven by a centralized dispatch process run by the ISO that also computes 5-minute and hourly locational spot prices.

The need for the operation of fossil fuel plants (coal, oil, and gas) depends on how much solar and wind power is available. We prefer that wind and solar operate whenever they are available because their marginal operating costs are very low. The California ISO has a website *(http://www.caiso.com/Pages/TodaysOutlook.aspx)* where you can see today's changes in demand and the availability of renewable resources minute by minute (see Figure 1-4 for a sample).The information is also available as a smartphone "app."

Generally speaking, the ISO has control over only the large producer side of the system. Customers make their own operating decisions. They decide when they turn on the heat or operate the air conditioning. Some attempts are made to control or at least modify customer devices. For example, customers are asked to reduce usage on extremely hot days when air conditioning demand is high and the electricity system is stressed.

The relationship between investment and operating decisions in the current business model is shown in Figure 1-5. It is noteworthy that this model evolved during a time when generation availability was predictable (no wind and solar) and customers had no information about the hour-to-hour cost of their electricity use.

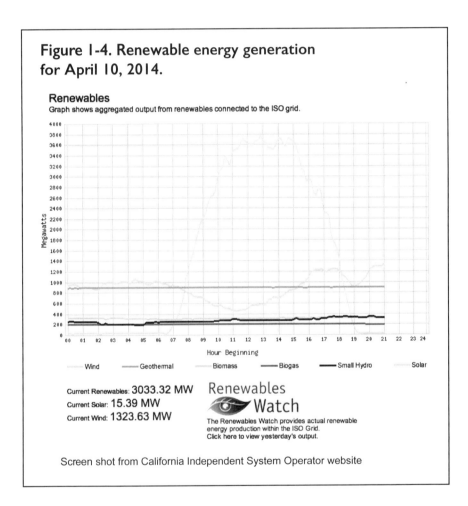

**Figure 1-4. Renewable energy generation for April 10, 2014.**

Regulators are struggling to make this model work in the new energy ecosystem. ISOs and utilities are asking customers to allow their devices to be controlled by ISO dispatchers. This is called direct load control (DLC). Other systems are experimenting with time-of-use (TOU) pricing to encourage some customers to change behavior in a way that lowers system operating costs or improves reliability.

Figure 1-5. Decision diagram for investment and ope~
decisions in the year 2000.

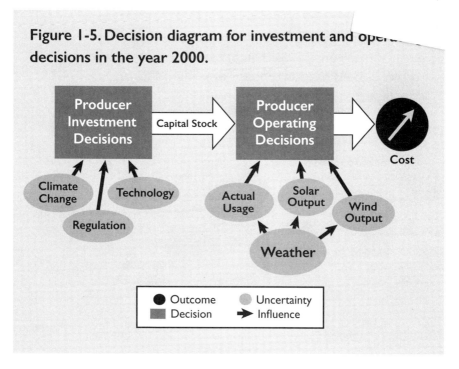

The TE model is different. The TE model uses forward- and spot-priced tenders among producer and consumer parties to coordinate investment and operating decisions throughout the ecosystem (see Figure 1-6). Tenders are priced offers to buy and sell energy-related products. The tenders are posted on Transactive Energy Platforms. When one party accepts the tender of another party then a transaction is recorded between the parties to produce and use energy.

Investments are made by producers, consumers, or prosumers, where they are the most profitable given current tender prices. Long- and short-term usage shifts to when low-price energy is available and from times when energy is highly priced. Investment and operating decisions are made autonomously, subject of course to environmental regulations.

Customers are constantly making energy investment and operating decisions. They decide which energy-efficiency devices to buy, and they decide how to operate the devices. Once they buy these devices, they operate them based on spot tender prices. In the TE model, customers as well as producers are able to use forward transactions with others to coordinate investments with others and manage risk. This is shown conceptually in Figure 1-6.

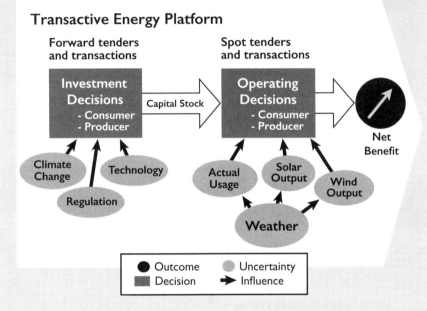

Figure 1-6. The TE business model uses forward tenders and transactions to coordinate investment decisions and to manage risk. Spot tenders and transactions are used to coordinate operating decisions.

## The TE Regulatory Model

The TE regulatory model follows the structure and operation of the TE business model that we have begun to describe. The TE business model requires less intervention by regulators in market operations. The TE model promotes more competition and standardization of transactions. This facilitates efficiency and innovation.

Some aspects of the TE business model such as electricity transport may naturally be provided by legislatively granted franchise owners. In this case the transport service is priced and transacted as cost-based services where the tariffs and recovery of costs is overseen by a regulatory body. Alternatively, the transport service is provided by a government-owned utility.

In many cases such as for California IOUs, the regulatory process is overly complex, burdensome, and costly. Each of the three main IOUs have about 70 tariffs. And there are programs and proceedings to address resource adequacy, capacity, flexible capacity, demand response, renewables portfolio standards, electric vehicle service, community-choice aggregation, DER interconnection, smart meters, energy efficiency, and much more. There are also proceedings of the California Independent System Operator (CAISO) that are overseen by the Federal Energy Regulatory Commission. These hearings concern many of the same issues faced by the IOUs, such as transmission planning, access and pricing, and wholesale spot market operation.

As we have begun to describe, the TE business model simplifies electricity commerce and makes it more transparent. The TE business model relies on more standardized interactions among wholesale and retail participants. This simplifies the task of regulation. This also releases regulators to focus on enforcing standards and contracts. The TE model facilitates fair and open transaction platforms. Fair market rules bring all buyers and sellers together, big and small, wholesale and retail, to do commercial business using standard business transaction processes.

TE Platforms provide regulatory transparency by recording all the information associated with consumer and producer forward and spot transactions. With this increased transparency, regulators will be in a much better position to know when markets are working well and when and where to intervene.

There will be a continuing need for oversight of reliability such as by the North American Electric Reliability Corporation (NERC). NERC develops and enforces reliability standards for the bulk electric grid. In addition, there will be a need for other grid custodian roles as well. These can all be accommodated within the TE business model.

## How Does TE Work?

In the TE model, investment decisions are guided toward economic equilibrium by forward tenders and transactions. Operating decisions are guided by the spot market tenders and transactions.

The TE process can operate in several ways and it will be mostly carried out by automated agents for the parties. The basic process is straightforward.

Producers signal to the customers that they have energy to sell by offering sell tenders (see Figure 1-7).

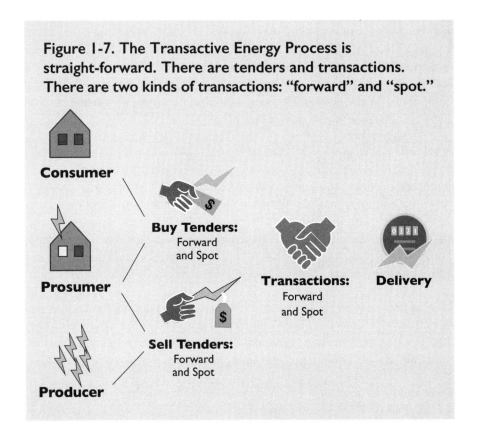

**Figure 1-7. The Transactive Energy Process is straight-forward. There are tenders and transactions. There are two kinds of transactions: "forward" and "spot."**

Consumers decide if they want to accept a portion of a sell tender at a tendered price, wait for a better tender, or not use as much energy.

For example, a sell tender might be: "I offer to sell 10 megawatts (MW) of electricity at my plant in Modesto, California, between 9 and 10 a.m. on Monday, January 2016. My sell price is $75 per MWh." This means 10 MW for 1 hour or 10 megawatt-hours (MWh) of energy is available.

If a consumer agrees to buy 2 MW of the 10 MW tender, then there is a transaction recorded between the buyer and the seller; the seller later delivers the 2 MW of electricity for the specified hour and the buyer pays the seller the tendered price of $75 per MWh times the amount transacted (2 MWh), which is $150.

Prosumers, such as homeowners with PV panels, can also accept sell-and-buy tenders from producers. Consumers and prosumers also make buy-and-sell tenders.

Producers, consumers, and prosumers can transact bilaterally or autonomously on the TE Platforms. The transactions are recorded and the energy is delivered. Balancing parties stand by to make alternate delivery for any transactions that producers fail to make and absorb deliveries that customers fail to use.

There are two products: energy and transport service. Customers will transact for their energy needs and separately transact for transport. (see Figure 1-8).

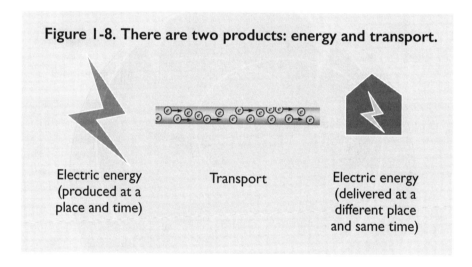

### Figure 1-8. There are two products: energy and transport.

Electric energy (produced at a place and time)

Transport

Electric energy (delivered at a different place and same time)

The grid has complex limits on how much electric energy can be transported from one location to another. There are losses in transporting the energy. Energy is transacted at specific locations, such as at a home, substation or generator.

Transport allows a party to arrange and pay for delivery of energy from one of these locations to another. Wholesale parties in the United States participate in similar transactions for energy and transport today.

Energy services parties and transport services parties meet on TE Platforms where they agree to transactions that may be facilitated by various intermediaries (see Figure 1-9). The transactions are recorded and all the parties operate their devices and systems autonomously. Operators will monitor the flows of electricity and arrange additional spot transactions to further balance the system within the various physical and reliability constraints of the grid.

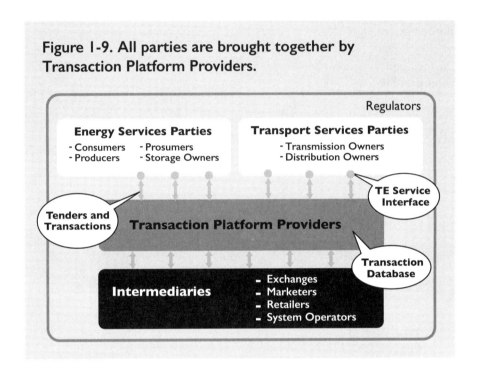

**Figure 1-9. All parties are brought together by Transaction Platform Providers.**

The TE approach has one big advantage: It provides a framework for coordinating both consumer and producer investments and operation. The investment decisions are made on a level playing field in a commercial market rather than by central planners. The result is an efficient, cost-effective system.

Producer and consumer forward and spot transactions are made on the same platforms. Consumers can transact directly with producers by purchasing energy and the necessary transport. Producers can sell directly to consumers who have access to transport.

There is one market rather than separate wholesale and retail markets as we have today. For each producer, intermediary, and transmission and distribution operator, there needs to be only one tariff for energy and one tariff for transport.

## Both Customers and Producers Can Manage Risk Using Forward Transactions

IOUs today enjoy a franchise granted to them by the California legislature that allows them to pass on the risk of certain investments and contracts to their customers. If the regulator approves the investment or contract as prudent then the IOUs investors will be allowed to recover their investment through consumer tariffs. This contractual arrangement lowers the risk of the investment to the utility and reduces the cost of financing. The theory is that lower financing costs are passed on to the customer in the form of lower prices. However, this model also passes all of the risks to the customers while providing little or no recourse for the customer to help reduce the risk, such as by shifting usage from high-cost times to low-cost times or selling power to the utility when the customer can sell for less.

In the TE model, both customers and producers have access to forward transactions or subscriptions for managing investment risk. For example, if a homeowner is contemplating installing solar panels then they can secure a forward transaction for the excess energy provided by the panels. They will be able to make good estimates of the savings and lock in future prices using forward transactions tied to the actual output of the panels. Despite how complicated the energy investment might become, the risk can be managed using forward transactions.

## All Parties Act Autonomously

Individual customers and producers have the best understanding of their needs and the best understanding of their market situation. People like to make decisions quickly in response to events like changes in the weather. Businesses want to act in response to customers and suppliers.

TE puts the end user in complete control of energy use: how much, when, and where. The customer can program energy devices like air conditioners or clothes dryers to respond to household or business needs and make cost-benefit tradeoffs accordingly.

Many IOUs attempt to control demand by offering customers incentives to accept demand reductions. This is a way of decreasing demand during peak periods. It may not be the most beneficial way of lowering demand. If loads are interrupted then something has to change on the customer's side of the meter, e.g., a production line has to be shut down or a household's comfort levels changed. When the ISO interrupts service it does not know the cost of the interruption; only the customer knows.

In the TE model customers and producers will move demand away from expensive times and toward inexpensive times without outside intervention. They have the economic signals they need to plan ahead. They are able to do what is in their interest.

## The Architecture of a TE system

There are three primary groups or parties in a TE system: energy services, transport services, and intermediaries. Energy services can be comprised of customers, producers, prosumers, or storage owners. Transport services are transmission or distribution owners. The intermediaries include exchanges, market makers, retailers, and system operators (see Figure 1-9).

The three groups or parties interact with each other and the system operators through transaction platform providers. Parties submit tenders and receive tenders through the TE Platforms to buy and sell energy and transport. Accepted tenders are recorded as transactions on the TE Platforms. The system operators do their work using transaction information available on the TE Platforms and from meters, other sensors, and models.

As shown in Figure 1-9, the arrows indicate two-way communication of tenders and transactions among the parties. The tenders and transactions are communicated using a simple TE protocol similar to that used in some financial markets.

A TE service interface is needed if a party controls devices such as generators or appliances, or if the party controls systems such as buildings, distribution grids, or transmission grids. The TE interface is where the control of party-owned devices and systems is carried out in response to priced tenders and to satisfy the transactions agreed to by the parties. Interval meters will record actual energy and transport flows over these interfaces.

We can move to the TE model in incremental steps. Most systems are modular and scalable. Some of the intermediary functions exist today, particularly in wholesale electricity markets. The technology to make the TE model work is available today.

# The Internet of Everything

The TE model would not have been practical just 20 years ago. It would have been too difficult to implement and too expensive. Things have changed. Advances in communication and information technology (CIT) have driven down the cost of computing and connection. Today, it is possible for a single customer to have the same CIT power that the ISOs have. Customers have access to decision-making processes that are as sophisticated as producers and ISOs.

Customers don't have to spend many hours trying to figure out what the best price is; when to buy or sell; or when to use electric energy. Smart devices can do that for them. Smart algorithms in smart devices will act as their agents.

The new smart thermostats offered by Nest Labs are just a glimpse of what is coming. The thermostat senses the location of homeowners and occupants and the logic in the thermostats "studies" their energy-use preferences. The thermostat also has access to energy prices and weather forecasts. Using this information, the device "learns" how to control heating and cooling in a way that balances comfort and cost. The thermostat is controlled through the user's smart phone from anywhere in the world.

Automobile manufacturers are also putting smart energy management logic into electric vehicles. Electric vehicles will tell the vehicle to charge and discharge its battery in a way that minimizes the owner's energy bill. The vehicle's energy management system will determine whether it should charge at home or in the office parking lot. It will even decide if it can profitably sell some of its stored energy back into the grid.

The TE model not only makes the best use of the new technology to increase efficiency and lower cost. Deployment of CIT will also spur innovation in the same way the Internet and cheap computing power has spurred innovation in many business and residential sectors.

## TE Responds to the Changes in the Electricity System

### Wind and Solar

Wind and solar generation are characterized by high investment cost and very low operating costs. The outputs are variable. Power is only available when the sun shines or the wind blows.

In the TE model, wind and solar investors use forward transactions to sell the actual outputs of the plants before they are built. The buyers take into account the daily and seasonal patterns of the energy supply and their forecasted energy needs. The buyers know they will be able to adjust for unpredictable shortfalls or excess power transactions by using spot transactions. Sometimes buyers will adjust their usage patterns to synchronize with sun and wind patterns in order to access the inexpensive, renewable energy. Demand moves toward the low-cost wind and solar energy.

## Storage

In the TE model, storage investors will see the variability of wind and solar as an opportunity. They will set the size and location of their units to manage variations in solar, wind, and end-use load. They will use forward and spot transactions to optimize the operation of the storage.

TE will encourage the installation of storage in the right places because energy and transport are treated separately. The storage can be large, megawatt-scale storage or storage installed by PV owners.

## Decentralized Energy Resources (DERs)

DERs operate on a level playing field with all other buyers and sellers in a TE system. They realize the benefit from their location in proximity to buyers and/or sellers. In many cases they will have an advantage because of transport savings. The same applies to homeowners with PV panels. They will realize the advantages of their location. When they purchase power from the grid they will pay their share of distribution and transmission costs. Everyone is made whole.

## Microgrids

Organizations such as universities or cities will choose to become microgrids because they see benefits from planning and operating independently. The benefits may be efficiency, financial, political, or educational.

The TE business model is scalable. Microgrids can use the TE model internally to plan investments and operations. The TE concept will enable microgrids to engage with the grid voluntarily for economic or reliability reasons. The grid can also use microgrids to improve reliability, particularly in the case of major catastrophes.

## Electric Vehicles

The electric vehicle will benefit from the TE model. The storage benefit of the electric vehicle will be integrated into the grid along with other storage. Vehicle owners will be able to minimize energy costs by charging their batteries when and where it is most convenient and economic. Charging within neighborhoods will be managed in a way that distribution impacts are reduced.

# Evolution Toward TE Is Inevitable

The benefits of TE are manifest and its implementation is eminently feasible.

## TE Will Spur Innovation

Once buyers and sellers have ubiquitous communication and real-time cost information they will be able to capture all sorts of new value for customers and providers, old and new.

The Nest Learning Thermostat is just one example of the possibilities.

## TE Will Make It Significantly Easier to Meet Our Efficiency and Environmental Goals

California has embarked on an ambitious effort to reinvent its electrical power system, moving from a system predominantly dependent on fossil fuels to one that increasingly emphasizes renewable energy. TE will facilitate that effort by making it easier to integrate renewable investments into the system and operate them effectively.

TE also helps customers (residential, commercial, and industrial) identify the best conservation investments. The TE system will allow us to make smarter investment and operating decisions across the board.

Imagine, an electric-vehicle owner going on vacation. While he is gone, the storage capability of his car's battery will be operated as an integral part of the electricity grid, shifting demand from one time to another and providing backup power. The car will sit in the garage making money for the owner and, at the same time, reducing waste on the grid. It might even reduce the need for local distribution investment. It will be lowering overall energy costs for society. A win-win for everyone.

## TE Is Fair

Two of the guiding principles of residential-rate design in California are the following:

- Rates should be based on marginal costs.
- Rates should be based on cost-causation principles.

TE is completely in accordance with these principles—certainly more so than our current top-down command-and-control systems.

In a recent Public Utilities Fortnightly interview *(http:www.fortnightly.com/fortnightly/2013/03/turning-energy-inside-out)*, Dr. Amory Lovins of the Rocky Mountain Institute (RMI) described it succinctly, "We're moving into an era where all ways to make or save energy will get to compete fairly, at honest prices, regardless of their type, technology, size, location, and ownership." The Transactive Energy business model meets the RMI vision.

## TE Is Transparent

The rules of TE are simple and unambiguous: forward and spot transactions between empowered players. Our current electricity tariff structures are complex and obscure. Attempts to respond to changes in the market often result in making them more complex. In the TE model everyone has the same tariff—forward and spot transactions for energy and transport.

## Summary

TE offers a vision that is efficient, fair, and transparent. Customers and producers, no matter what size, play by the same rules. Costs are allocated fairly by an open, commercial process. The whole system is operated on consistent and transparent principles.

TE also offers resilience and adaptability. Like the World Wide Web, the TE system is self-healing. It is able to adjust instantaneously to changes in equipment and routing availability. Micromarkets are able to work independently or as an integral part of the grid. The TE model also adapts to economic, technical, and social changes in an organic way.

In a nutshell, forward and spot transactions can be the glue that holds together the system of wind, solar, decentralized power, central power plants, storage, microgrids, and other elements we have not considered yet.

We don't expect the change to the TE model to happen overnight. But it has started. It will continue if we proceed with caution and systematically remove obstacles to innovation.

## The Rest of This Book

The Transactive Energy vision is described in more detail in Chapter 2.

The TE model rests on three pillars: systems, connection, and protocols. Each pillar is described in Chapter 3.

In Chapter 4 we explain how TE responds to the challenges and opportunities in the electric power markets.

Chapter 5 answers the question, "Why Transactive Energy?"

Chapter 6 addresses the question, "How Do We Get There from Here?"

The authors qualifications are reviewed in Chapter 7.

**CHAPTER 2**

# The Transactive Energy Vision

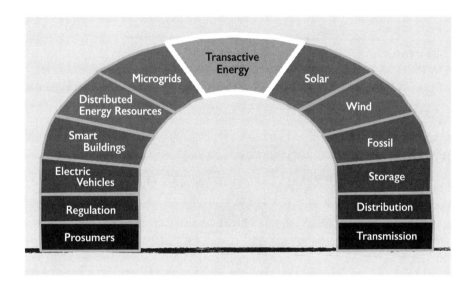

In this chapter we explain the fundamentals of the Transactive Energy (TE) business model. We begin with an example of a transactive model that many people know well: buying and selling tickets to a baseball game. We then explain the TE business process: tenders, transactions, and deliveries in Section 2. There are two kinds of transactions: forward and spot. In Section 3 we explain how these transactions are used to coordinate investment and operating decisions throughout the electricity system.

# Background

## Overview

1. The Transactive Energy business model is not new.

2. StubHub, the marketplace for event tickets is a good example of how the transactive business model is evolving in complex markets.

Voluntary transactions between buyers and sellers are the linchpin of our economy. They are the basic building blocks of commercial markets.

Markets of various kinds have evolved to match buyers and sellers. If the product is retail groceries the buyer goes to the grocery store and shops. If we are trying to buy a house we usually go to a real estate agent. The realtor's job is to match up buyers and sellers.

The Internet and e-commerce have enabled some very interesting market innovations. These innovations have resulted in more profit for sellers, more convenience, lower costs, and less risk for buyers. The market for baseball tickets is a good case study of how markets are evolving.

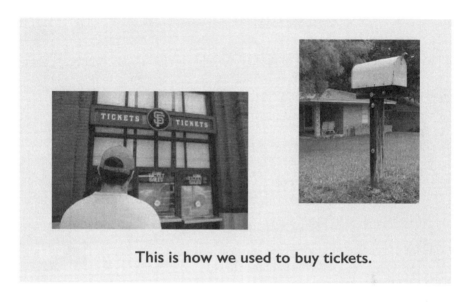

### This is how we used to buy tickets.

Before the year 2000 the only way you could buy a ticket to a baseball game was by going to the ball park on game day or by purchasing it in advance by mail. There was one transaction. You bought a ticket. The baseball team had your money.

Prices were printed over the ticket booth and they were fixed. If I wanted a special seat then I had to go early. Not much flexibility.

In the year 2000 baseball teams started selling season tickets on the Internet, which quickly evolved into a system of selling tickets to individual games using the Internet.

Today I can go to the San Francisco Giants' website and buy tickets to any game. There is an added wrinkle. The baseball team owner is now able to maximize profit by adjusting the price of the tickets. The price goes up if demand is high, or if there are only a few tickets left. Prices increase more if the Giants are winning, there are only a few tickets left, the weather is good, and the game is imminent. The price decreases when there are lots of unsold tickets and the game is about to start. All price adjustments are made by sophisticated revenue management algorithms. The pricing is done in a way that maximizes owner revenue.

Now, suppose I have a ticket and something unexpected comes up at work. I am unable to go to the game. The tickets are not refundable. Perhaps I can give them away or find someone who will sell them near the stadium on game day (e.g., a scalper).

I am no longer a ticket buyer. I now have a ticket to sell. I am probably not alone. Many people buy season tickets so they get good prices and are assured of getting a "favorite" seat. They don't go to all the games, so from time to time they would like to sell their seats rather than leave them empty.

In about 2000 a couple of Silicon Valley entrepreneurs spotted a need that they could fill. They started an Internet-based company called StubHub. Stubhub has become the ticket scalper of the digital age, the ultimate middleman to shift the way people interact to buy and sell tickets to almost any concert, theater performance, or sporting event.

StubHub is now an online transaction platform. They provide services for buyers and sellers of tickets. Stubhub has grown from the largest secondary-market for tickets in the United States to the world's largest ticket marketplace. It is said to process one sports or entertainment ticket every second and in 2012 had approximately 15 million unique visitors per month.

As of September 2013, StubHub has more than 120 partners, including Anschutz Entertainment Group, the O2, Staples Center, Major League Baseball Advanced Media, 28 Major League Baseball Clubs, ESPN cable TV network, more than 35 NCAA premier colleges and universities, a number of NHL, NBA, and MLS sports teams, as well as some of the top music venues in the United States and Europe. Internationally, StubHub also has partnerships with several Barclay's Premier League teams and has partnered with Crown Talent and Media Group to become the official ticket seller for some of its artists.

## How Does Stubhub Work?

Today when I want to go to a baseball game I go straight to the StubHub website *(http://www.stubhub.com)*.  I click the right menus for buying Giants tickets and I see the whole ballpark laid out on the computer screen. I begin the buying process by selecting the number of seats I want and I specify a "price level." This is used to narrow down the options.

I also notice on the screen the statement, "Market pricing applies to all tickets. Buy early and save. Prices subject to market demand." I have to decide, do I buy now or wait? If I think the game will be a sell out, then I will buy now. If I think the game will be undersold then I will wait for ticket prices to drop as game time approaches. I can use my knowledge and preferences to reduce my costs and risk.

Along with more convenience, the Internet and e-commerce have offered me more information and more options. But it gets even better.

Suppose, I buy a ticket and I cannot go to the game. This seems to happen from time to time. Friends get sick. Work gets in the way. No problem. I go back to StubHub and sell my tickets. The proceeds are deposited in my PayPal account.

I can do the transaction on my smartphone. StubHub.com even offers tutorials on how to get the best price for your tickets.

StubHub is now an online transactive ticket platform. StubHub does not own the baseball park or the team. StubHub simply provides a convenient place to make matches between ticket buyers and sellers. It provides a place for them to offer buying or selling tenders and consummates transactions online, 24/7.

## Summary

Here are some of the things I can do with Stubhub:

• Tender offers to buy tickets for a section of the ballpark in a price range.
• Tender offers to sell tickets that I hold for a price. I can change the price and withhold the sale at the last minute.
• I can buy a season ticket and sell tickets to individual games I can't use. This limits my risk.
• I can request seats near friends.
• Buy, sell, and deliver tickets from my smartphone or other mobile device.

Our objective here is not to promote either the Giants baseball team or Stub-Hub. Our objective is to illustrate how a transactive business model works to increase efficiency and reduce risk for both buyers and sellers.

Season tickets and other advance sales are forward transactions. StubHub trades near game time are spot transactions. The combination of forward and spot transactions provides efficiency and risk management.

StubHub illustrates how easy it is for a single consumer to participate in a complex market by using the transactive model. It is easy to make buying or selling tenders and to complete transactions.

Forward and spot transactions coordinate decisions by owners and fans. All the market players interact smoothly. Costs are low and customers are getting services they did not have before. There are fewer empty seats in the ballpark. It is easier for the owners to sell season tickets and reduce their business risk. The physical facilities are the same, they are being utilized better, and more efficiently.

The TE business model can bring to electricity what StubHub brings to baseball. The TE model holds the promise of providing electric energy buyers (customers) with the ability to find the lowest cost seller(s) to meet their needs. It also provides buyers and sellers clear price information on which to base their long- and short-term decisions. It limits risk for everyone, not just producers.

The amazing thing about StubHub is that the physical system is unchanged. A transaction management platform has been added. The same is true for the electricity system. In the short-term the physical system stays the same. It just operates more efficiently. In the long-term, the system is constantly evolving in the direction of efficiency and overall lower costs.

StubHub succeeded because they entered the transaction market first. However, the system remains open to innovation. There are no barriers to other entrepreneurs entering the market with better products or even the same products. There will probably be as many StubHub-type online services as there are markets. In fact, we expect there will be many "StubHubs" in electricity markets. And we believe that is a good thing.

SECTION 2

# The Process: Tenders, Transactions, and Deliveries

## Overview

1. A tender is an offer to buy or sell something.

2. A transaction is a buy or sell agreement.

3. There are two products: energy and transport services.

4. There separate transactions for energy and for transport.

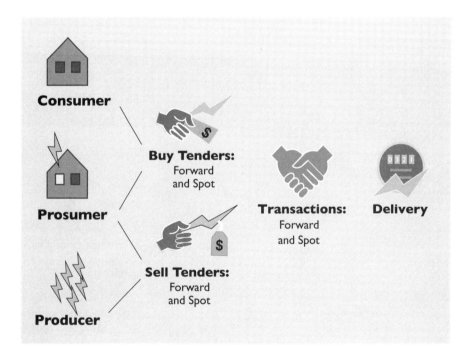

The TE process is straightforward. There are electricity buyers and electricity sellers. Buyers make tenders to buy the energy they want to meet their anticipated energy needs. Sellers make tenders to sell the energy they have. We have a transaction when a buyer or seller accepts a tender.

The tenders and transactions take place on a TE Platform either bilaterally or in exchanges. Historically, exchanges have been buildings, like the Minneapolis Grain Exchange. TE Platforms can be virtually anywhere and they can host multiple exchanges. Most likely they will be software applications in the "Cloud."

The TE system is dynamic. After a buyer has transacted for his anticipated energy needs, then he has a position in the market. If something better comes along or his energy needs change, then the process repeats itself until the buyer attains a better position. The same goes for sellers. Transactions can continue right up to the time the delivery is made.

In a TE system all the tenders and transactions take place very fast. Computational speeds are beyond comprehension, and according to Moore's Law, computation capability per dollar doubles every 2 years. The technology for monitoring, predicting, and managing energy is accelerating. The Nest Learning Thermostat (discussed in Chapter 1) is an example of what is already available.

One of the benefits of the transaction speed and volume that technology allows is that large transactions can be replaced by many small transactions. A buyer can automatically accumulate a forward position in a series of small transactions. This reduces risk and provides more feedback between buyers and sellers. Parties can buy a little energy, then some transport, then more energy, and then more transport. The energy and transport providers will not sell more than they can provide at the prices that customers are willing to pay.

Once the positions of the buyers and sellers are established, then deliveries can be made. Responsibility shifts from the transaction system to the physical system.

The forward positions of the buyers and sellers are more than financial positions. Parties will make investment decisions, schedule business operations, buy fuel for generators, start up and ramp generators, store energy for later delivery, and much more based on the forward transactions. During the actual delivery interval, possibly 5 minutes or less, a system operator may monitor the overall balance of supply and demand on the grid. The operator may issue tenders that cause generators and customers to buy or sell energy. For those parties that do not exactly balance their metered delivery with their forward positions in an interval, they will pay the system operator or be paid at the spot price.

# The TE Tendering Process

TE is designed so that any party (consumer, producer, or prosumer) can be a buyer or a seller at different times. Customers may accept or make tenders to buy energy to meet some of their needs months and years in advance. Forward transacting is a way of managing the risks in their electric bills. Typically, customers will want to accept the lowest-priced sell tenders or the highest-priced buy tenders offered to them in a given interval of time.

A customer's energy management system (EMS) will frequently evaluate its energy use based on weather forecasts, predicted heating and cooling needs, other factors, and the prices of current forward tenders. It will accept tenders that will optimize the operation of the customer's devices to the benefit of the customer.

As the time for delivery approaches the tenders the customer receives will be driven more by the spot market. At the "moment" the energy is needed the consumer will be ready to pay the prevailing spot price, forego purchase, or sell back some from a previous position. Again, the logic of this choice will be programmed into the EMS and some devices. For example, the consumer's dryer could say, "Find me the best time to run the dryer within the next 4 hours that will cost the least."

Large generators and transport providers can afford to put more effort into posting spot and forward tenders. They are the primary source of tenders that buyers can accept to create transactions. Intermediaries such as marketers and retailers may accept some seller and buyer tenders and then resell their accumulated net positions to provide tenders to others. Market makers may be licensed and paid to continuously and automatically post small buy-and-sell tenders in forward intervals with a small spread between their buy-and-sell prices. The more buyers and sellers in the market, the more fair the tender prices will be.

# Parties Who Buy and Sell Energy and Transport

The buyers and sellers of electricity comprise the following groups or parties: individuals, families, businesses, and governments. At the smallest level, an owner might buy energy to charge an electric car. The vehicle can interact directly with a TE Platform on behalf of the owner to buy energy. The vehicle has a battery where it can store energy. The vehicle owner might buy energy during some periods and sell energy during other periods. The actual buying and selling is managed by the EMS onboard the vehicle. Automobile manufacturers are already installing the electronic systems to interface with the grid.

At the other end of the size spectrum a buyer can be a single owner of a whole microgrid. The microgrid can be a university campus, a military installation, or a municipality. The microgrid plans and operates its own energy system. However, from time to time it might need energy from the grid, or it might want to sell energy into the grid. It can do so. Microgrids with multiple parties may transact with each other within the microgrid and with other parties outside of the microgrid.

In other words, the TE business model is scalable. Scalability is valuable in systems. The Internet is scaleable. A website can be as small as one person's blog or it can be as large as Amazon.

It is the same for sellers. The seller can be the owner of a single electric vehicle sitting in a garage with energy in its battery, or the seller can be the owner of a wind farm or a nuclear power plant. Moreover, a party can take on the role of buyer or seller. A producer may buy back energy previously sold and the customer may sell back energy previously purchased as tender prices change and needs of the parties change.

## Buy Tenders

When a buyer in the TE system needs energy or transport, they may accept a standing sell tender from another or issue a buy tender to one or more other parties. For example, "I need 1.5 kWh delivered every hour of every day for the next five years to run most of my appliances and HVAC." Or an aluminum smelter might make a tender for 10,000 kWh (kilowatt-hour) every hour. A buy tender specifies how much, where, and when. Each tender goes to a TE Platform and it is recorded in the platform along with all the other tenders.

## Sell Tenders

Sell tenders are the mirror image of buy tenders. Someone has energy to sell at a time and place. The seller can be a single homeowner with a PV panel. The homeowner's EMS has a weather forecast and it predicts that the PV panels will produce more energy than the homeowner needs. With the help of the EMS the homeowner will offer a tender to sell the predicted excess hour by hour.

A wind farm will tender energy at the times the operators think the wind will be blowing. A nuclear power plant will tender to sell a nearly constant stream of power.

# Transactions

An energy transaction is defined as an exchange among two parties of energy for a payment. Buyers and sellers use the buy-and-sell tenders to initiate transactions in much the same way Stubhub arranges ticket sales and purchases. Stubhub supports many ticket sales and purchases, but they do not go to any baseball games. They make their money from providing a service. They are a transaction platform.

TE Platforms will have rules to govern what constitutes a valid transaction. Fundamentally, it is a contract. For example, Ajax Wind Farm agrees to sell 100 kWh of electricity to the University of California, Davis, between 1 a.m. and 2 a.m. on July 10, 2016. Ajax is confident that the wind will be blowing at that time and the University is sure they will need the power at that time The weather, however, can be uncertain.

If the wind isn't blowing on July 10 then Ajax will have to go back to the TE Platforms to buy enough energy to meet the terms of their transactions. Their obligations will be met through a combination of forward and spot transactions.

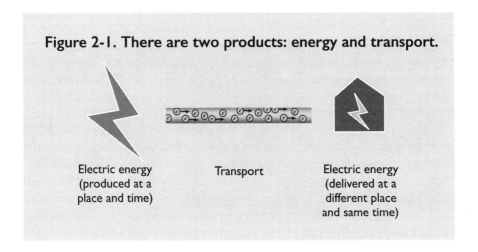

Figure 2-1. There are two products: energy and transport.

Electric energy (produced at a place and time)     Transport     Electric energy (delivered at a different place and same time)

## Two Products: Energy and Transport

There are two products in a TE system: energy (at a time and place) and transport (see Figure 2-1). Buying energy in the TE system is like buying a book on the Internet. The book is purchased from the Amazon website and the transport is arranged with UPS. The product and the transport are provided by separate businesses.

The delivery of electricity is done over transmission and distribution lines. These are owned by a variety of organizations, including investor-owned utilities (IOUs), the federal government, and local municipalities.

When a customer wants energy they may make or accept two tenders: one for energy (at a time and place) and one for transport.

Compared to buying and selling baseball tickets this may seem overwhelmingly complicated. It is a complex system. However, the principles on which it operates are not complicated. High frequency markets are a matter of fact in banking and other financial industries. Most of the decision-making is done by agents and algorithms in the Internet framework according to agreed upon standards. TE works the same way.

## The TE Platform

Every participant is connected to at least one TE Platform where business is done (see Figure 2-2). Information on tenders and transactions is stored in a database associated with each transaction platform.

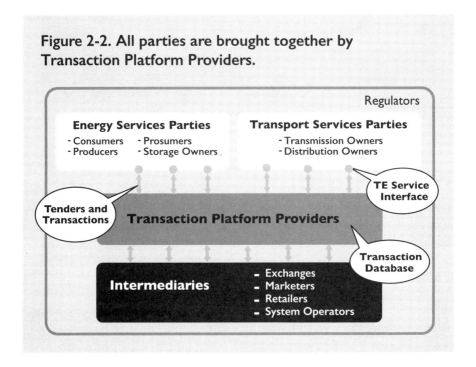

**Figure 2-2. All parties are brought together by Transaction Platform Providers.**

There are three types of groups or parties in the TE model that do transactions: energy, transport, and intermediary. Additionally, there are parties that provide the transaction platform but do not participate in transactions. Finally, there are regulators that will monitor transactions but not participate in transactions. All use a TE protocol to communicate tenders and transactions with each other.

The physical side of the system includes the energy services and the transport services. This includes any party who produces, consumes, or transports electricity. All physical parties involved in energy deliveries use a TE service interface to work with tenders and transactions with other parties. Energy and transport service providers will also have interval meters to measure actual deliveries.

Intermediary parties, including exchanges, marketers, retailers, and system operators, are connected to the TE Platform in much the same way we connect to a social network on a platform such as the career website LinkedIn.

Regulators access the TE Platform so they can detect economic abuse and determine whether everyone is playing by the rules. Regulators will be able to use very sophisticated analytics to do their job.

## Summary

The TE business process is straightforward. Buyers and sellers communicate their needs with tenders offered and accepted on TE Platforms. Transactions are facilitated by exchanges, market makers, and other intermediaries. There are two products: energy and transport.

Energy services, transport services, and intermediaries communicate using tenders and transactions recorded on Transaction Platforms.

Forward and spot transactions are used to coordinate investments and operation throughout the system. We discuss the functioning of forward and spot transactions in the next section.

SECTION 3

# Forward and spot transactions

## Overview

1. Two kinds of decisions are made in the electricity ecosystem:

   • Investment
   • Operating

2. Forward transactions are used to coordinate investment decisions and to manage risk.

3. Spot transactions are used to coordinate operating decisions and mitigate risk.

*The TE model uses forward transactions to coordinate investments and manage risk. Spot transactions are used to coordinate operating decisions and mitigate risk.*

Forward and spot transactions are used throughout the TE system to coordinate investment and operating decisions. Traditionally, major electricity investment decisions have been made by utilities and large generating companies with the approval of state and federal regulators. Operating decisions have been made by Independent System Operator (ISO) and integrated utilities. Customers and decentralized energy resources (DER) have operated largely on the basis of fixed-kWh price tariffs offered by IOU or municipal utilities or approved energy retailers. (see Figure 2-3).

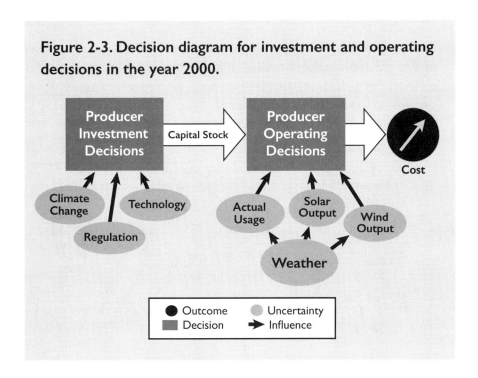

**Figure 2-3. Decision diagram for investment and operating decisions in the year 2000.**

This arrangement is becoming increasingly problematic because supply is shifting from conventional central generation (coal and oil) to renewables and customer investment in DER. The decentralized investments are becoming more important to our goals of improving efficiency and decreasing $CO_2$ emissions. (We discuss all of these challenges and opportunities in more detail in Chapter 4.)

In the TE business model, forward transactions are used to coordinate investments throughout the electricity ecosystem. Retail customers, prosumers (both customers and producers), and decentralized energy producers use the same platforms to develop forward buy-and-sell transactions (see Figure 2-4). Everyone plays on a level playing field.

Any investor can use forward transactions to manage price and cost risk. Currently, IOUs and independent power producers can use long-term contracts to reduce risk. These contracts are a form of forward transactions. In the TE model retail customers would use subscriptions to manage risks associated with investments in such assets as PV panels or efficient appliances.

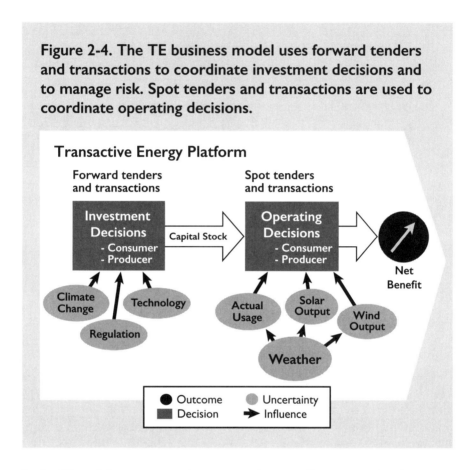

**Figure 2-4. The TE business model uses forward tenders and transactions to coordinate investment decisions and to manage risk. Spot tenders and transactions are used to coordinate operating decisions.**

In the TE model, spot transactions are used to coordinate operating decisions. Again, all parties, big and small, have access to the same spot transaction exchanges. In the current model, only large wholesale and industrial customers use a spot transaction system to coordinate operations.

All investment and operating decisions are autonomous. Producers and consumers decide what to invest in and how to operate it. Their autonomous decisions are coordinated because they use common tenders and transactions recorded on the same transaction platforms.

The responsibilities of economic regulators will remain the same as today. Regulators are responsible for ensuring that rules are followed and that there are no economic abuses.

Next, we discuss the investment and operating decisions in more detail. We explain how the investment decisions are made and how forward transactions are used by producers and consumers to manage risk.

# Large Producer and Consumer Investment Decisions

Long-term contracts and subscriptions are familiar forms of forward transactions. A long-term energy contract promises to deliver something in the future for a prespecified price. It is a way of assuring consumers they will get what they want and at the same time it reduces risk for the investor.

Industrial customers are reluctant to build a new manufacturing plant if they are not confident they will have the energy they need. Likewise, private investors are reluctant to build multimillion-dollar generation facilities in today's uncertain environment unless they are confident they will make a profit.

IOUs and municipal utilities have used the regulatory umbrella provided by government to shield them from most technical and market risks. The agreement between IOUs and regulators is: "I will build the plant, and spot prices will be enforced in a way that my investors will earn a fair return." This agreement lowers risk to the IOU. Lower risk means lower interest rates on borrowed money. Some of the lower interest rate savings are passed on to customers. However, the risk is also passed on to the customers and today they have little opportunity to reduce their risk.

Cash flows are the language of finance. Transactions coordinate investment decisions and are used to manage risk. The approach is the same whether the investment is a nuclear power plant or an efficient refrigerator.

For example, a sophisticated investor begins evaluating a project by laying out the year-by-year cash flows into and out of the project. Figure 2-5 shows the cash flows for a typical power plant, such as a combustion turbine or a wind farm. The components of the calculation are as follows:

1) Initial investment (negative cash flow).

2) Revenues from sales, which are typically the most important and the most uncertain (positive cash flow).

3) Expenses: fuel, maintenance, taxes, etc. (negative cash flow).

4) Terminal value: what we can sell the asset for at the end of its useful life (positive cash flow).

The major "risk" is typically in item (2), the revenues from sales. If this is too small, the project will lose money.

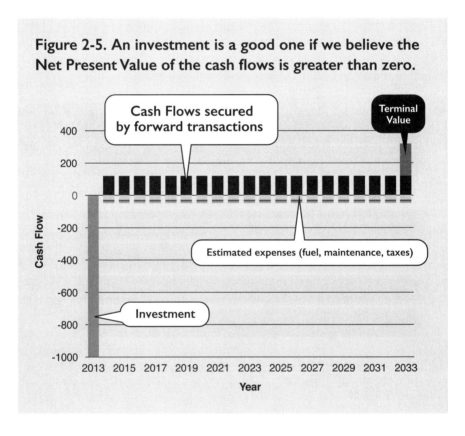

**Figure 2-5. An investment is a good one if we believe the Net Present Value of the cash flows is greater than zero.**

Forward transactions are used to remove much of the uncertainty in the revenue cash flow. The seller estimates what he can produce and "tenders" to sell to other parties on a TE Platform. If one customer, or ideally many customers, transacts for the energy, then the project investor has a predictable cash flow for the next 10 or 20 years. Market risk is significantly reduced.

Projects are evaluated using the concept of net present value (NPV) of cash flows. Theoretically, if the NPV is positive then the investment is a good one. At least it is better than leaving the money in the bank. (For background on NPV we recommend an introductory course in finance. Coursera offers a good one from the University of Michigan. It is free.)

Forward transactions or long-term contracts reduce the uncertainty in the revenue cash flow. This also lowers interest rates on borrowed money and makes projects more profitable. The same logic applies whether it is an investment in a combustion turbine, a wind farm, or a massive solar installation. The availability of forward transactions enables investors to predict profit and thereby manage risk.

## Small Producer and Consumer Investment Decisions

We believe that most investments in the new ecosystem will be made by consumers, prosumers, and owners of decentralized energy resources. These investments will be needed to attain our efficiency, environmental, and reliability goals.

Subscriptions are a form of forward transaction. When I subscribe to a magazine I promise to pay for a year's worth of issues for a prespecified amount of money. Payment is made up front. This reduces risk for me and also for the magazine publisher. I am sure I will get every issue of the magazine delivered to my door in a timely fashion. I pay less than I would pay if I bought the magazine at the newsstand. Thus, the subscription is a forward transaction that guarantees service for a prespecified price.

If I miss an issue of The Economist because I am on vacation or I want an extra issue to give to a friend, then I can buy it at a newsstand. Of course I pay the newsstand price, which is substantially higher than the subscription price. The newsstand is a sort of spot market. It serves people who don't want or have a subscription.

In the TE model, retail customers can subscribe for electricity. This gives retail customers access to the same economic advantages and risk reduction mechanisms that are currently available to large producers.

Consumer subscriptions for energy and transport are transacted on the same TE Platforms as large producer forward transactions. The sharing of TE Platforms supports ecosystem-wide coordination.

Cash flows for a consumer investment in an efficient device, such as an efficient air conditioning system, are shown in Figure 2-6.The key elements of the cash flow are the following:

1) Initial cost of the unit (negative cash flow).
2) Tax credits or subsidies (positive cash flow).
3) Operating cost savings (positive cash flow).
4) Terminal value: increase in the value of the property when it is sold (positive cash flow).

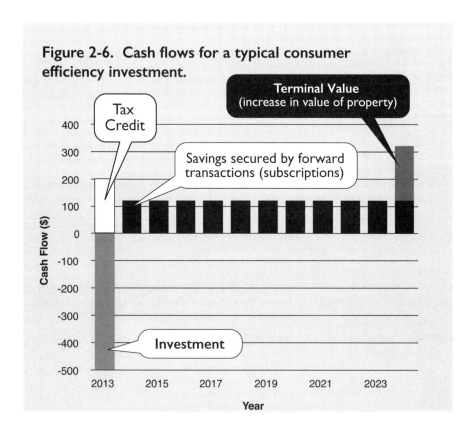

**Figure 2-6. Cash flows for a typical consumer efficiency investment.**

It is the savings that are uncertain and they drive a consumer's decision to invest. Savings are often published on appliances, but these are merely estimates based on average use and projections of future energy prices. These are uncertain.

Access to a subscription or forward transaction gives the customer a way to remove most of the savings uncertainty. Again, this makes it easier to make the efficiency investment. It reduces the risk for small players in the same way forward transactions reduce risk for large investors. The playing field is leveled and it will certainly result in more consumer investments in efficiency.

Investment dollars flow to where they produce the most profitable investments in efficiency. An innovation could be a new solar facility, insulation for a home, a storage battery, or a gas-fired combustion turbine. As prospects for the future change, the system rapidly adapts to the new realities. Innovations just happen. Customers and investors are free to decide which innovations they want.

In the TE model, homeowners buy and sell energy using forward transactions on the same TE Platforms as producers. The playing field is level. Furthermore, small customers can use the same risk-management approach that large producers and consumers use.

## Operating Decisions

Ultimate savings or profit depends on how a device is operated. The operation of major appliances like heaters and air conditioners is unpredictable primarily because of the weather. Weather determines heating and cooling demands. Weather is becoming increasingly important because it drives the availability of wind and solar energy. We need spot transactions because it is impossible to predict future needs and supplies with absolute certainty. If a producer cannot deliver on a forward transaction because of unseasonably bad weather, then the producer can buy energy on the spot market to meet his contract obligations. Likewise, if a customer undersubscribes for energy, then they can make up the difference by buying on the spot market (see Table 2-1).

| Table 2-1. Comparison of decision making | | |
|---|---|---|
| Decision | Transactive Energy | Current system (Cost of Service) |
| Producer Investments | Forward transactions used to determine profitability and reduce risk. | Investor owned utility investments approved for inclusion in rate base. Any investment in rate base is guaranteed fair return. |
| Consumer Investments | Forward transactions (subscriptions) used to determine savings and reduce risk | Based on estimates of future cost-of-service pricing and subsidies. |
| Producer Operating | Spot prices for Energy and Transport. | Least Cost Based |
| Consumer Operating | Spot Prices for Energy and Transport | Cost of service based. Flat, fixed price tariffs. |

The difference between a customer's actual demand and forward position is shown in Figure 2-7. At 12 o'clock the demand exceeds the amount of energy subscribed for (the forward position). This is not a problem, as the customer's EMS simply buys the difference at current spot tender prices. Likewise, early in the morning the customer has oversubscribed so he has energy to sell at current spot tender prices.

IOUs in California are struggling to adjust time-of-use (TOU) tariffs to give the proper signals for customer decision-making. This is an impossible task. Things are changing so fast planners cannot keep up. For example, it used to be that the hottest summer day determined the highest demand for the year and this was a day with marginally high-priced energy. The oversimplified logic was that new generation would have to be built to meet this demand.

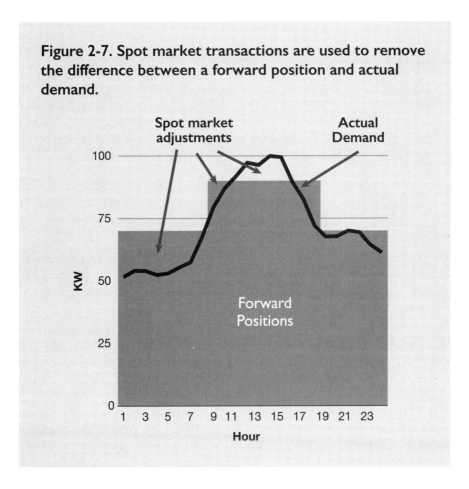

**Figure 2-7. Spot market transactions are used to remove the difference between a forward position and actual demand.**

The new reality is that the energy supply from solar nearly coincides with the highest demand for cooling. (It's hot because the sun is shining.) If enough PV panels are installed then the peak demand hour may have a surplus of energy and the tender prices may be low, zero, or negative. Now what do we do?

With the TE model this is not a problem. Energy usage moves away from times when energy is scarce and expensive and toward times when energy is abundant and therefore cheap. It does this without any outside intervention.

Although investments in gas turbines and wind farms get most of the attention, consumer investments will account for most future improvements in efficiency. These investments run the gamut from big process change investments by industrial customers to residential customer investments in efficient appliances, PV panels, and insulation.

In a TE system consumers have the same sophisticated operating logic available that producers have. Each household, or conceivably each smart appliance, will have a position for each hour prior to the start of each day. This is the amount of energy they have transacted or subscribed for using forward transactions. The position will depend on a number of factors:

• The thermodynamic characteristics of the house.
• Expected occupancy.
• Weather forecasts.
• Consumer preferences for comfort or convenience.

There will almost always be a difference between actual demand and customer's position. Suppose weather is hotter than expected. The air conditioner will have to run more than expected to keep the house at the "perfect" temperature.

In this case, the EMS will buy more energy on the spot market to run the air conditioner more or it will turn up the thermostat. This decision will be made automatically based on preset consumer preferences and logic.

Sometimes homeowners will oversubscribe for power. This is not a problem in the TE model. The excess energy will be sold on the spot market. If the selling price is higher than the homeowner paid for their subscription, then they will have a profit. A smart EMS might actually be able to make money for the homeowner or prosumer.

We can imagine how complicated the operating decisions become when we have to pick from the full gamut of energy storage and production options: PV panels, smart appliances, and battery storage. The beauty of TE is that the EMS has all the market information it needs to maximize net benefit for the homeowner and do it in a way that is coordinated with all the other producers and consumers.

Consumers will probably sort themselves out into "passive" and "active." Some customers with small bills and little interest in managing their electricity usage will choose to do business much the way things are done today. They will likely opt for a subscription that satisfies their needs and pay a bill every month.

Automated interactions will appeal to a group of "active" energy users. These customers will have larger energy demands and they will have invested in equipment to improve efficiency (see Figure 2-8). Generally, they will have an EMS that makes the operating decisions in real time. These systems are effectively acting as their agents.

## Summary

Tenders and transactions are used to coordinate energy and transport decisions. There are two kinds of transactions: forward and spot.

There is no difference in the way producers and consumers participate in the system. The logic of buying and selling energy and transport is the same for all parties. The decisions on what energy supply system is built and how it is operated is ultimately determined by the commercial transactions among the parties and the autonomous decision-making of the parties.

Forward transactions are used to coordinate investments throughout the system and to manage risk. They are used by both producers and consumers for both energy and transport investments.

All parties use spot transactions for operating decisions. Spot transactions are used to coordinate producer and consumer operating decisions. The parties include producers, prosumers, consumers, and owners of decentralized energy resources. They also include owners and operators of storage. The storage can be a huge pumped hydro facility or the battery of an electric vehicle. The operating principles and rules are the same.

Coordination is provided by TE Platforms. Both forward and spot transactions are recorded on the same platform. Currently, we have more-or-less open wholesale energy and transmission platforms but no open platforms for commercial and residential customers.

## Figure 2-8. Here's an example of how Transactive Energy works for a consumer.

• Based on my typical usage, I automatically transact with a supplier for delivery of a fixed quantity of energy in each hour of the year(s) for a fixed monthly payment (subscription.)
  • If I use less than I subscribed for in each hour then I am paid for the difference at the hourly spot price.
  • If I use more than I subscribed for then I pay for the difference at the hourly spot price.
• As my needs change, at any time I can automatically buy or sell a quantity of energy at the current spot price tendered by my supplier(s).

All the decision making is handled by an algorithm in my energy management system. The energy management system is my agent.

Risk management is provided using forward transactions to lock in future revenues and savings. Here again, both producers and consumers have access to the same risk management opportunities. Currently, wholesale producers use long-term contracts and regulatory covenants to manage risk. Consumers are left to their own devices.

The services are scalable, that is, they can apply to a microgrid or to an entire geographic region. The first pilots of TE may be large microgrids.

The TE business model may deliver an example of what ecologists call "emergent behavior." Emergent behavior arises when all the individuals in a group follow a few simple rules without any central coordination. This is the behavior exhibited by flocking birds or schooling fish. In the case of TE a few simple rules followed by autonomous parties can lead to collective behavior that is efficient and adaptable. The "few simple rules" are that producers maximize profit using forward and spot transactions and consumers maximize benefit using forward and spot transactions.

The differences between the way decisions are made in the current cost-of-service and the TE model are summarized in Table 2-1. The differences are apparent and it is easy to see why the TE business model has the potential of delivering a more efficient system and ultimately reduce our dependence on fossil fuels.

Forward transactions allow everyone to manage risks and smooth out revenues and expenses. Spot transactions make the system adaptable and responsive to changes in weather, fuel costs, and random events.

As we shall see in future chapters, TE takes advantage of the revolution that has taken place in communication and information technology. Residential customers will have sophisticated energy management systems that help them decide how to make investments and operate their equipment.

# Transport

## Overview

1. Transport and energy are separate products in the TE model.

2. TE can solve many problems associated with transport:

- Spot transport transactions can be used to avoid local congestion.
- Forward transport transactions (subscriptions) can be used to assure recovery of fixed transport costs.

3. Forward and spot transport prices are based on location pairs. This does the following:

- It rewards proper placement of storage and generation.
- It promotes efficient use of the available transport infrastructure.
- It guides investment in transport.

The TE model separates transport from energy. Buying energy in the TE model is like buying a book on the Internet. The book is bought from a vendor, like

Amazon, and the transport of the book is arranged with a delivery service, like UPS. The book and the transport are separate products. The total price to the customer is the price of the book plus the price of shipping and delivery. TE works the same way for electricity.

A customer's energy management system (EMS) automatically evaluates energy tenders and the transport tenders to deliver the energy. The EMS can compare alternative suppliers by comparing the total price of delivered energy. Total delivered price equals energy tender price plus transport tender price (see Figure 2-9).

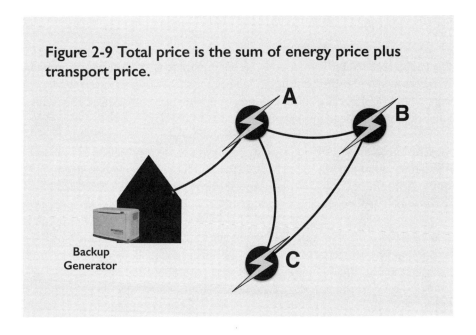

**Figure 2-9 Total price is the sum of energy price plus transport price.**

For example, the customer's EMS can buy energy from locations A, B, or C on the grid or use its backup generators. The total prices are the sum of energy tender prices at each location and the transport tender price to move the energy from each location to the customer's home as seen by the customer's EMS during a specific interval of time (see Table 2-2; the total "home" price of $50 is the cost of running the backup generator). Clearly, since location C shows the option with the lowest total price (see Table 2-2), the EMS will buy energy there and buy location-to-location transport from C to its facility.

| Table 2-2. Energy and Transport Prices | | | |
|---|---|---|---|
| **ENERGY LOCATION** | **ENERGY PRICE AT LOCATION** | **TRANSPORT PRICE TO THE HOME** | **TOTAL PRICE** |
| **Home** | 50 | 0 | **50** |
| A | 38 | 4 | **42** |
| B | 30 | 7 | **37** |
| C | 30 | 3 | **33** |

Electricity is delivered over a network of transmission and distribution lines, transformers, and other equipment. These networks are owned by a variety of organizations including IOUs, independent transmission owners, the federal government, and local municipalities.

Most networks are alternating current. Energy flows along parallel paths according to the laws of physics. In the case of the purchase of energy from location C, some of the energy will flow from C to A to the home and some from C to B to A to the home. Real networks have thousands of such links and nodes.

The customer EMS does not need to how much of the energy will flow on each link or line. The customer's EMS only needs to know transport tender price from each location to the customer's home. The EMS picks the pair of energy and transport tenders that has the lowest delivered price. The tenders are all posted on the TE Platform.

## Management of Transport Capacity Limits and Energy Losses

The capacity of networks is determined by the capability of lines and devices that comprise the network. TE tender location-to-location prices signal when congestion is present somewhere on the network. Generators and customers use the tenders to adjust generation and/or loads to avoid congestion.

Transport operators are responsible for monitoring the actual energy flows into and out of the network at each location. They can also compute, and in some cases monitor, the flows on each line, the transformers, and other devices on the transport network. An algorithm will assist market makers to adjust the transport tender prices up or down at each location so that customer's and generator's EMS systems will adjust how much they use and generate at each location.

Transport prices also include the marginal cost of the next increment of network losses to move energy from one location to another on the network. Power lines and equipment heat up when transmitting energy. The heating causes energy losses. The energy loss tends to be proportional to the square of the quantity of energy flowing on the network. Doubling the flow quadruples the loss.

Average transport losses are about 7%. If networks become congested, the incremental losses can rise as high as 40% between some pairs of locations. If this happens, supply C may not be the lowest price alternative and supply A may become more attractive (see Table 2-2). The customer EMS does not need to know what is happening on the grid. The EMS only needs to know location-to-location transport prices given to them by the TE Platform.

## Forward Transport Subscriptions and Spot Transactions

Forward transactions and subscriptions for transport offer an economic mechanism for customers and suppliers to contract for a fixed amount of transport at a known price.

Forward transactions and subscriptions help in coordinating additions to the transmission and distribution grids with the willingness of customers and supplier to pay for them. A project to add capacity to the grid will allow the sale of more subscriptions for transport. If customers and suppliers are willing to buy the subscriptions, then investors will invest in the new capacity.

Spot transactions coordinate operating decisions in ways that minimize transmission and distribution losses. Customers are constantly using spot energy and transport tenders to select the lowest total energy and transport price location to buy their power. When a network gets congested, then the transport operators will adjust location-to-location prices to reduce congestion (see Figure 2-10). Network operators will use sophisticated algorithms to determine spot tender prices.

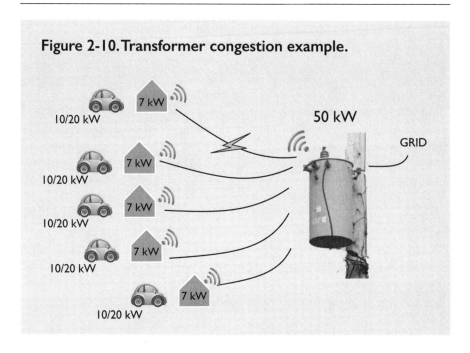

## Figure 2-10. Transformer congestion example.

An example demonstrates how the TE model can coordinate system adjustments in a neighborhood that has several fast charging electric vehicles.

A cluster of five homes is connected to a single 50-kilowatt (kW) transformer. Each owns a Tesla Model S. The vehicle batteries require about 8 hours of charging at 10 kW (single charger) or 4 hours at 20 kW (double charger) for a full charge. The required charge depends on daily mileage. If all five homes charge at the same time, the transformer will be overloaded and there will be no transformer capacity to serve other uses of electricity in the homes.

Let's assume that each of the five homes pays for a 10 kW transport subscription that enables the home to transport 10 kW at any time from the transformer to the home. If all the homes use no more than their 10 kW subscription in an interval there should be no problems. However, if two of the homes want to fast charge their cars at 20 kW then there might be a problem.

Each home has an energy management system (EMS) and there is a micro TE Platform at the transformer. The TE Platform communicates forward transport tenders for each 15minute interval for the next 24 hours to the home EMSs. Transport tender prices are adjusted up or down by the transport market maker's algorithm up until there is no congestion. Customers can sell some of their

10 kW of transport to neighbors when they need less. They can buy transport when they need more.

If the aggregate needs of the five customers cannot be met, then the customers may ask the transport provider to upgrade the transformer capacity to 100 kW. Each home will subscribe to an additional 10 kW of transport and each home will pay an additional fixed monthly payment to cover the costs of the new capacity.

This model has the advantage that capacity is only added if it cannot be avoided by smart management. Another advantage is that the consumers contract to pay for the new capacity at the time it is installed. Additionally, it is the consumers who benefit who pay for the incremental new capacity. The system is efficient, fair, and transparent. In addition, if a customer sells his Tesla he is still obligated to pay for the transport, but he can sell it to a neighbor who wants more capacity.

Suppose that some of the five homeowners also have PV panels and batteries. Now it is possible that the EMSs will support bilateral energy transactions between neighbors to reduce the need for transport. The cluster of five homes will become a small grid. Each EMS will manage the in-home use, the charging of the car, and the charging and discharging of any in-home storage. The EMS will also manage buying and selling of energy with suppliers on the other side of the transformer and/or with their other four neighbors. The neighborhood will exchange price information with the outside world through a system-wide TE Platform on the other side of the transformer. An advanced version of this setup might have switches, protection, and control so that when the main grid goes down from a storm, the local neighborhood could continue to operate serving critical load from the PV, the car storage, and other storage and backup generation.

It sounds complicated. The complication is managed by computers, algorithms, and communications systems that the customers never see. The EMSs simply carry out the will of their owners. They act as the agents of the owners.

## Importance of Location Effects in the Electric System

Storage can reduce the need for transport if it is located properly. Storage can shift transport demands from one time to another. Typically, storage is charged at night when routine line loads are low. In this way, storage allows us to use existing lines more efficiently and reduce the need for new lines.

Decentralized energy resources (DERs) can also avoid the need for transport capacity. When electricity is produced close to where it is consumed there is less need for transport.

Forward transactions reflect long-term transport cost savings. If a battery can avoid new transmission lines, then the savings are reflected in forward tender values. The savings are captured at the time the battery investment is made. The same is true for DERs that avoid transport investments. In other words, storage and DER investors use forward transactions in the same way forward transactions are used by all producers and consumers to coordinate decisions and manage risk.

Spot transactions are used to coordinate storage and DER operating decisions. Central storage, DERs, and homeowner storage are connected to the same TE Platforms where they share buy-and-sell tenders.

## TE Solutions to Some Thorny Problems of IOUs

A large fraction of some customers' bills is fixed transmission and distribution charges. Figure 2-11 shows the current combined rate base for Pacific Gas and Electric, Southern California Edison, and San Diego Gas and Electric broken down by transmission, distribution, and energy (generation). The embedded fixed costs of transmission and distribution greatly outweigh the fixed costs of energy. The challenge of the IOUs is to recover all of these costs using the current regulated tariff models.

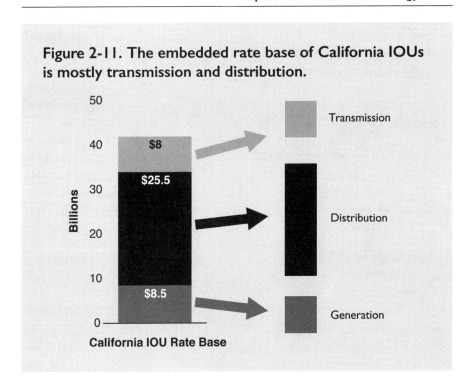

**Figure 2-11. The embedded rate base of California IOUs is mostly transmission and distribution.**

Customers can avoid paying the transmission and distribution costs by installing PV panels and batteries, They can go "off" the grid. As these self-sustaining customers leave, the fixed costs of distribution typically gets spread over fewer remaining customers, and the dollars per customer go up. This in turn makes it attractive for even more customers to leave, and the phenomenon has started what some describe as a "death spiral" (see Figure 2-12).

The TE model offers a way for IOUs to mitigate the "death spiral." IOUs can offer customers long-term (many years) forward subscriptions (paid monthly) for transport. This gives the IOUs a way to recover costs and spread costs fairly across the customer base. If customers decide to install solar and batteries they can sell and buy transport tenders according to their needs.

Those who decide to disconnect completely from the grid can sell their subscriptions to other parties. (There may be an abundance of new electric vehicle owners who need more transport capacity.) People who leave the grid and later decide to reconnect will be able to buy new transport subscriptions at whatever is the prevailing price, which could be high.

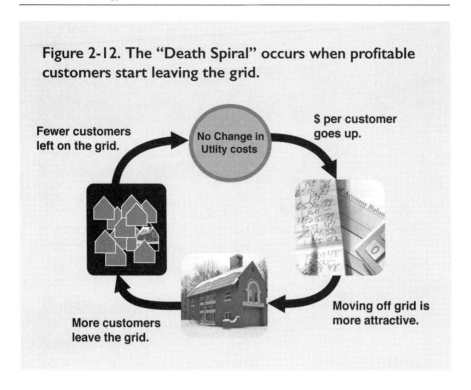

Figure 2-12. The "Death Spiral" occurs when profitable customers start leaving the grid.

Customers who reduce their transport subscriptions and self-generate can still access the grid. However, it may be expensive if they use the grid when transport prices are high. Spot-tender transport and energy prices will be allowed to be very volatile in a mature TE deployment. Customers are protected from big shifts in their bills because they buy and sell most energy and transport using long-term subscriptions. For these customers' spot transactions are only used to make modest adjustments.

## Managing the Transport Grid

With TE, distribution and transmission transport operators will continue to be responsible for the reliable operation of the networks. They will need to measure and monitor the state of their networks and manage devices and switches as flows change. They will maintain instrumentation and communication so that they can monitor congestion and overloads.

For the foreseeable future, large generation units will continue to be centrally dispatched by ISOs and regional transmission operators (RTOs) or vertically integrated utilities. Producer and consumer EMSs will make spot transactions to avoid overloads.

Transport operators will only tender a portfolio of subscriptions that can be delivered reliably. If at any time they cannot reliably support contracted subscriptions, they will buy and sell spot and long-term subscriptions to restore reliability.

## Summary

When we separate transport and energy into two distinct products, then we can use the TE model to coordinate investments and operation of transport in the same way we do for energy. Forward subscriptions are used to coordinate transport investments and manage risk. Spot transactions are used to coordinate the operation of transmission and distribution.

The total delivered price to the customer is the sum of energy and transport transaction prices. Consumers and producers of all sizes work within the TE Platforms to find what combinations of energy supply and transport are best for them. The TE model and automation simplifies a very complex delivery problem.

This way of handling transport enables the efficient placement of storage and DERs. Devices close to customers realize a benefit from lower price for transport. With the TE model in place, we will install as much storage and DER as is profitable and efficient. There is no need to determine what is "optimal."

CHAPTER 3

# The Three Pillars: Systems, Connection, and Protocols

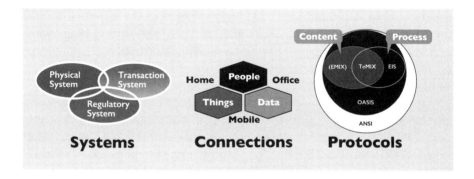

Transactive energy (TE) is an evolution in the way we do electricity business. In order for the business model to work we need three things: systems, connections, and protocols. Three systems support the TE business model: the transaction system, the physical system, and the regulatory system. The systems require connections and protocols to function. Moore's Law and the Internet have provided more than enough connection. Standard TE protocols are defined and are being deployed. In this chapter we explain these three pillars.

SECTION I

# Transactive Energy Systems

## Overview

1. There are three systems in the TE business model

   • Physical system
   • Transaction system
   • Regulatory system

2. The physical system includes energy generation, storage, transmission, and distribution, together with energy-use devices such as heaters and air conditioners.

3. The transaction system involves exchanges, market making, arbitrage, hedging, and financial services.

4. The regulatory system safeguards against economic abuse, rule violation, and oversees safety and reliability.

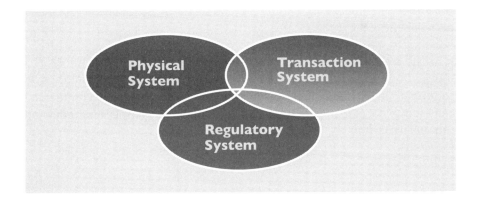

TE business model consists of three distinct systems: the physical system, the regulatory system, and the transaction system. Most people are familiar with the physical system: the network of electricity generators, storage, transmission lines and power poles, and the energy-using devices like heaters and air conditioners.

The physical system is the same in the TE model as it is today—except that it is evolving quickly with more decentralized generation and storage and more variable renewable generation.

The instant a customer flips a light switch the light comes on in the room. This has to be done without overloading any link in the system; the quality of the power (voltage and frequency) has to be maintained; routine system reliability has to be maintained; and someone has to be available to respond to catastrophes.

System operation might seem like an insurmountable task given the millions of customers and thousands of energy sources. It is a challenge. Nonetheless, it is done with amazing performance. In the United States we have come to regard reliable electric service as a fact of life. Our operating systems rarely break down; however, when they do from natural- or human-caused disasters the consequences can be enormous.

The function of the regulatory system is the same in the TE model as it is today. Electricity is such an important part of our social, economic, and environmental fabric that federal and state governments play an important role in its planning and operation. The role of regulators is to ensure rules are followed without abuses of economic power. Additionally, the regulators oversee the safety and the reliability of the system.

It is the transaction system that needs explanation in this book. The transaction system uses forward and spot tenders and transactions to coordinate investments and device operation. This system of commercial contracts replaces a system of legislatively enforced spot prices for retail and commercial customers.

## Transaction System

The transaction system begins with the energy service parties. These are the consumers, producers, prosumers, and storage owners. They compliment the transport service parties: transmission and distribution owners.

System operators are an intermediary entity (see Figure 3-1). Energy and transport parties, along with system operators, are brought together with other intermediaries on platforms provided by TE Platform providers (see Figure 3-1). The intermediaries include exchanges, marketers, and retailers. Arbitrage, hedging, market making, and financial services are provided by the intermediaries.

### Figure 3-1. The Transaction System

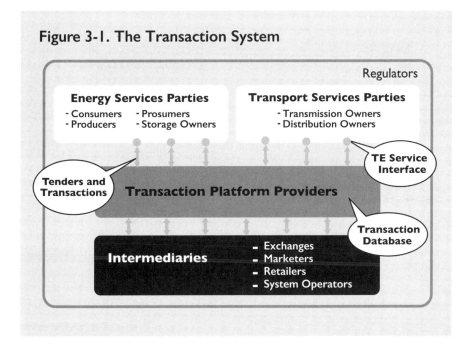

The TE Platforms bring together buyers and sellers. TE Platforms are where parties create buy-and-sell tenders. The tenders are made available to other parties to accept and create transactions. They provide the same service that Stubhub (*www.stubhub.com*) provides for sports events, concerts, and theater tickets.

E-commerce has revolutionized transaction platforms and exchanges. In the past, exchanges were buildings, like the Minneapolis Grain Exchange (a beautiful piece of architecture). Today, exchanges are very different. Exchanges are software applications ("apps") located in the Cloud, or a remote network server. They operate semi-autonomously using a set of algorithms. Humans design, implement, and oversee these **apps**.

Stubhub is a good example of how transaction platforms and exchanges have evolved. The service was started after 2000. It is enabled by the Internet and sophisticated database management systems. It's easy for buyers to tell the system what they want, when, and where they want it. They tell Stubhub generally where they would like to sit and/or what they are willing to pay. Sellers tell the exchange what they have and what price they are willing to sell. Algorithms in the Stubhub software record the tenders and interact with buyers and sellers to find matches.

Stubhub also manages the transfer of money from buyer to seller, usually through a third party. Someone, usually a third party, ensures that buyers are able to pay. In Stubhub this is managed by a network of financial services firms such as PayPal, Visa, and MasterCard.

The TE Platforms act in the same way. TE Platforms are where customers and producers go to offer tenders. Exchanges are linked to the TE Platform that in turn is linked to producers or customer energy management systems (EMSs) located throughout the grid.

TE Platforms also provide a place where intermediaries can bring together buyers and sellers with unique needs (see Table 3-1). The intermediaries also connect with their customers and the exchanges through the TE Platform. The intermediaries help small buyers or sellers transact by supporting a more liquid market where parties can frequently receive forward tenders. They also play a key role in assuming risks that others may not want to assume. For example, some intermediaries may buy long-term forward positions and then sell these positions closer to the time of delivery.

## Table 3-1. TE model activities

| TRANSACTIVE ENERGY PLACES AND ACTIVITIES | FUNCTION |
|---|---|
| Transactive Energy Platform | Places where buyers and sellers go to post tenders and accept tenders to form transactions. |
| Exchanges | Facilitates anonymous matching of buyers and sellers. |
| Market making | Provides liquidity to the market. |
| Clearing | Activities between transaction and settlement (includes, credit and collateral management, reporting and monitoring, tax handling, and failure handling). |
| Arbitraging | Closes differences in prices for energy at two different locations and the price of transport between the two locations. |
| Hedging | Risk management where forward transactions are used in place of uncertain prices of future spot transactions. |

Both energy and transport are traded at the platforms. This is much the same as the wholesale electric energy markets in California work today. The forward transaction platform is provided by bilateral contracts and on exchanges such as ICE (*www.theice.com*), and the spot transactions occur on a California ISO platform.

Market makers play the important role of providing liquidity to the market. Typically, a market maker will post relatively small forward buy-and-sell tenders with a small price spread (the spread is the buy/sell price difference.) The tenders will expire after a short period of time and during this time the market maker takes on the risk that counter parties will accept larger amounts of buy tenders than sell tenders (or vice versa). When this happens the market maker is left with net positive or negative positions. The market maker then decreases the prices of the next buy-and-sell tenders to reduce net positive positions (or raise the prices in the case of net negative positions). This iterative process drives the markets toward equilibrium. The market makers will typically use algorithms for these price adjustments.

The market makers are compensated by means of the price differentials for providing liquidity to the market, reducing transaction costs, and facilitating trade. The market makers are not producers or consumers and they should not be allowed to speculate for their own profit. Market makers should be licensed and regulated to make sure they act independently of other parties and do not manipulate the market for their own profit or for the profit of others.

The Nasdaq stock exchange is the prime example of a platform that hosts market makers. There are more than 500 member firms that act as Nasdaq market makers, keeping the financial markets running efficiently because they are willing to quote both buy-and-sell tenders for an asset.

**Clearing and other financial services:** In banking and finance, clearing denotes all activities from the time a commitment is made for a transaction until it is settled (the energy is delivered and paid for). Clearing of payments is necessary to turn the promise of payment (for example, in the form of a check or electronic payment request) into actual movement of money from one bank to another (see "clearing" in Wikipedia.)

In a market like electric energy, clearing is necessary because the speed of trades is much faster than the cycle time for completing the underlying transaction. Clearing involves the management of post trading as well as pre-settlement credit exposures to ensure that trades are settled in according to market rules, even if a buyer or seller should become insolvent prior to settlement. Processes included in clearing are reporting/monitoring, netting of trades to single positions, tax handling, and failure handling.

**Arbitrage**: In economics and finance, arbitrage is the practice of taking advantage of a price difference for the same good in two or more markets. The arbitrager strikes a combination of matching deals that capitalize upon the difference. The arbitrager's profit is the difference between the market prices. Arbitrage offers the possibility of a risk-free profit after transaction costs while at the same time helping the market to reach a more efficient equilibrium.

**Hedging** is a strategy for managing risk. In simple language, a hedge is used to reduce any substantial losses/gains suffered by an individual or an organization. People are hedging when they buy car insurance. They pay an insurance premium to avoid the risk of a complete loss of their car in an accident. In a TE system retail customers will be able to hedge against high prices with forward transactions.

Once a TE system is in place, then entrepreneurs will constantly respond to the need to make the transaction system more user-friendly, more efficient, and more reliable. Stubhub, the sports event ticketing service, provides a good example of how this happens.

Today, the wholesale market in California generally follows the TE model. Buyers and sellers enter into long-term forward transactions. The California ISO operates a spot market that trades in 1-hour and 5-minute blocks. Energy and transmission are transacted separately.

One of the limitations of the current ISO markets is the restrictions on which tenders they accept. They do not post forward tenders that commercial or retail customers can accept for transactions. The ISO markets may evolve to provide this functionally in the future.

The TE model will be implemented on multiple platforms, such as local retail platforms and regional wholesale platforms (see Figure 3-2). There will be energy and transport providers at all levels.

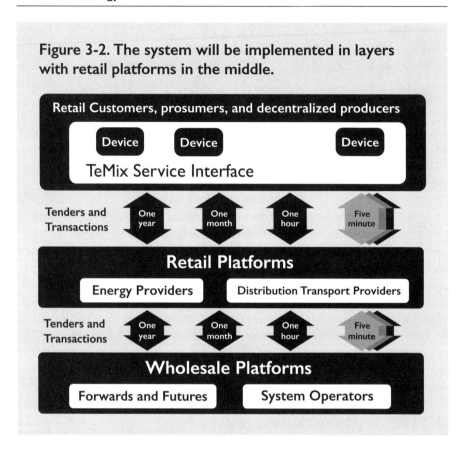

Figure 3-2. The system will be implemented in layers with retail platforms in the middle.

## The Physical System

The physical system consists of the wires, transformers, switches, generators, storage devices, energy-using devices and the associated automated and manual control systems. Someone has to operate each of the physical systems. Who is responsible for the wires, switches, and transformers? Making sure the power lines are not overheating? Who puts the system back together after a tornado?

In California we have transmission operators and distribution operators that are typically owned by the investor-owned utilities (IOU)—municipal and federal utilities that actually operate the transport equipment and devices. Generators and customers operate their own devices. The operation of generators and transmission is coordinated by the California ISO.

## Figure 3-3. Screen shot from California Independent System Operator (ISO) website. Plot shows impact of renewables on total demand.

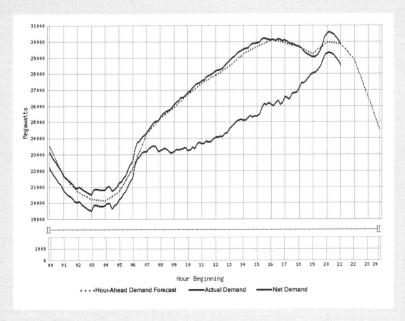

### Net Demand

The net demand curve depicts the variability in demand and supply that the ISO must counter balance in order to maintain grid reliability. Net demand is calculated by taking the actual demand and subtracting the electricity produced by variable generation resources, wind and solar, that are directly connected to the ISO grid.

Higher levels of variable electricity generation increases the ISO operational need for resources with the technological flexibility to start and stop quickly, and maintain output for set periods of time, so we can match supply and demand at all times.

The California ISO also operates spot markets in semi-TE fashion. The ISO receives day-ahead hourly and real-time, five-minute tenders to buy and sell energy at over 3,000 locations and matches buyers and sellers in an auction process that clears the market while respecting physical transmission limits, losses, and reliability constraints. The ISO posts the hourly day-ahead and 5-minute locational prices at each of its more than 3,000 locations.

The California ISO has an informative website where you can watch the hourly contribution of wind, solar, and other renewables and view the locational prices (see Figure 3-3 and the California ISO website (*www.caliso.com.*)

ISOs and regional transmission operators (RTOs) have spread to many regions of the United States and Canada as shown in (see Figure 3-4). ISOs and RTOs are essentially the same type of entity, except that RTOs may have more regional planning responsibility.

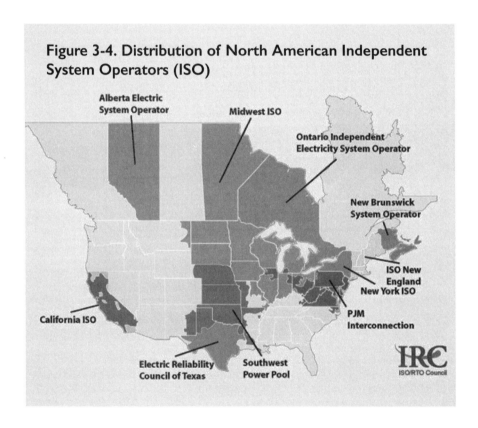

**Figure 3-4. Distribution of North American Independent System Operators (ISO)**

As shown in Figure 3-2, the ISO interacts with a retail energy provider in the TE system. The retail energy provider interface is currently needed because of the complexity of the ISO energy and ancillary services products, processes and settlement systems. The retail energy provider posts tenders to the TE service interfaces of retail customers, prosumers and decentralized producers as illustrated in Figure 3-2. Ultimately a complete TE implementation would allow wholesale and retail parties to directly transact while also transacting transport to move the energy between locations.

The relationship between energy management algorithms, the TE service interface, and the physical devices and systems is shown in Figure 3-5. The energy management system and TE interface can be in a device like a thermostat, a home computer, or the Cloud. Physical devices include air conditioners, electric vehicles, and decentralized generation like PV panels.

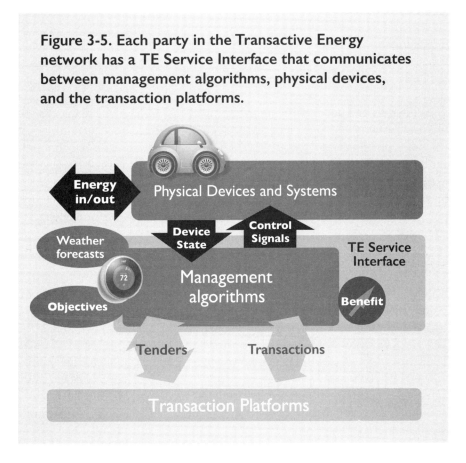

**Figure 3-5. Each party in the Transactive Energy network has a TE Service Interface that communicates between management algorithms, physical devices, and the transaction platforms.**

It is important to note that the customer's devices are controlled by the customer's energy management algorithm, not by the ISO. The ISO gets information about customer transactions through the TE Platform.

The energy management systems (EMS) will be connected to the Internet so they can monitor weather and other information relevant to building management. A Nest Learning Thermostat is an example of a device that is a simple yet sophisticated energy management system (EMS) that controls heating and cooling devices in a residence. All the logic and communication capability needed for TE can be contained in a device like a Nest Thermostat that is connected to the Internet to get tenders, weather forecasts, and other data.

Energy delivery will still be measured with an interval meter. The meter measures the energy flowing into and out of the devices on short intervals of time. For example, the intervals may be hourly, 15 minutes, 5 minutes, or 4 seconds, depending on the grid size of the customer or producer. The interval meter, which is sometimes called a "smart meter," will communicate meter readings to the TE Service Interface.

The TE model can be implemented with very few modifications of the current physical systems. It depends on the size and operational sophistication of the customer, prosumer, and producer. TE requires some investments in communication and information technology (CIT). Transport operators will have access to information about forward transactions as well as current energy flows base on sensors at all levels of this grid. Forward transactions for energy and transport will help them do a better job of planning and anticipating problems.

## Regulatory System

Regulators will always play a role in maintaining national security, public safety, protecting the health of the environment, and financial security. Electric power is vital to our way of life and our well-being.

The TE model greatly reduces the workload of economic regulators. The requirement for oversight on price setting is greatly reduced. There is only one tariff that applies to all customers. "Prices" for everyone are discovered through forward and spot transaction processes. The system is inherently fair and transparent.

Some oversight will always be required to safeguard against rule violation and economic abuses. This is true of virtually any market, such as stock markets and commodity markets. In particular the positions of large-market participants will need to be monitored closely.

The electric power industry has long been the focus of environmental regulation, and air emissions, water use, and pollution will continue to be regulated.

TE will facilitate the pricing of some externalities like carbon emissions. It is relatively straightforward to integrate a carbon tax into the forward and spot transaction process.

Public regulatory entities will also continue to be involved in the siting of power plants, transmission, and distribution lines.

## Summary

The TE model adds a new system to the electricity ecosystem. The heart of the system is the TE Platform where parties meet and arrange transactions.

The physical system remains unchanged. Energy service parties and transport service parties connect to the TE Platforms through a TE interface.

A variety of intermediaries will emerge to provide market services, such as exchanges and market makers. These are straightforward adaptations of services available in most commercial markets. Stubhub, the event ticket market, is one example—founded just 14 years ago and is still ubiquitous.

The regulatory system will continue to provide market oversight to safeguard against rule violation and economic abuses. Regulatory involvement in consumer technology decisions will diminish.

# Connection

## Overview

1. The Internet allows all parties to participate in TE.

2. Wireless (Wi-Fi) enables energy management systems to monitor and control devices.

3. Smart appliances and the smart home are ready for TE.

4. Smart meters allow the TE Platforms to confirm deliveries and initiate billing.

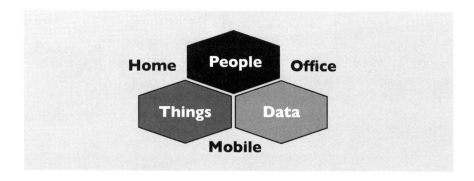

The Internet is now fast, universal, and wireless. The connection technology required for Transactive Energy (TE) is in place.

The Internet has connected American homes and businesses. The Internet enables two-way communication between all entities connected to the TE Platform. It also gives all devices access to information available on the Internet, such as weather and emergency warnings.

Within the home, local area wireless technology, or Wi-Fi, is enabling devices to communicate. The vision of the "smart" home is becoming a reality. People, data, and things are connected. Furthermore, they are connected at the office, at home, and on the road.

## Smart meter

Smart-meters availability is expected to reach 100% by 2020 in most developed countries—and is almost complete in the United States (see Figure 3-6). A smart meter is usually an electrical meter that records consumption of electric energy in intervals of an hour or less and communicates that information back to the utility for monitoring and billing purposes at least daily.

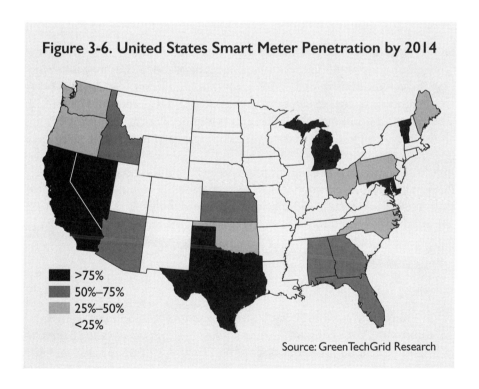

**Figure 3-6. United States Smart Meter Penetration by 2014**

>75%
50%–75%
25%–50%
<25%

Source: GreenTechGrid Research

Communication is a challenge for smart meters. Considering the varying environments and locations where meters are found, the problem can be daunting. Among the solutions are the use of cell and pager networks, satellite, licensed radio, combination licensed and unlicensed radio, and power line communication. Both the medium used for communication purposes and the type of network used are critical. These include fixed wireless, mesh network, or a combination of the two. There are several other potential network configurations possible, including the use of Wi-Fi and other Internet-related networks. To date no single solution seems to be optimal for all applications. Rural utilities have very different communication problems from urban utilities or utilities in difficult locations, including mountainous regions or areas ill-served by wireless and Internet companies.

## Internet Connection

The TE model capitalizes on Internet communication to connect the TE Platforms with all parties via TE Interfaces, and the EMSs. An EMS can be a device in the home or it can simply be an application operating in the Cloud.

More homes have Internet access than have smart meters. The Internet is broadband. Huge amounts of data can be sent back and forth among many parties. This opens up untapped opportunities for innovation (see Figure 3-7). We are already seeing thermostats that can be controlled remotely from iPhones. In this case, the thermostat not only has access to spot prices on the grid, it also has access to weather forecasts and even the homeowner's location via the Internet.

Individual devices like the electric car can also have direct access to the TE Platforms. The day may already be here when automobile manufacturers put EMS logic in electric vehicles. The EMS logic will coordinate charging and discharging with current and forecasted spot prices. Imagine an electric car sitting in a garage buying and selling energy on the grid while the owner is on vacation.

## Wireless (Wi-Fi)

Wi-Fi completes the link from TE Platform to EMS to smart appliance. According to a report by Strategic Analytics (*http://www.pcmag.com/article2/0,2817,2402672,00.asp*) the usage of Wi-Fi within US homes was about 60% in 2012 (see Figure 3-8.) That puts the United States eighth in the world, and far behind South Korea, whose ubiquitous broadband also means a corresponding bump in home Wi-Fi usage, at over 80%. It seems that Wi-Fi usage in the United States will approach 100% by 2020.

# Figure 3-7. Household computer and Internet Use (USA)

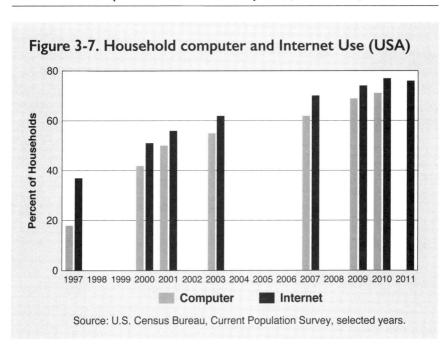

Source: U.S. Census Bureau, Current Population Survey, selected years.

# Figure 3-8. Percentage of households with WiFi

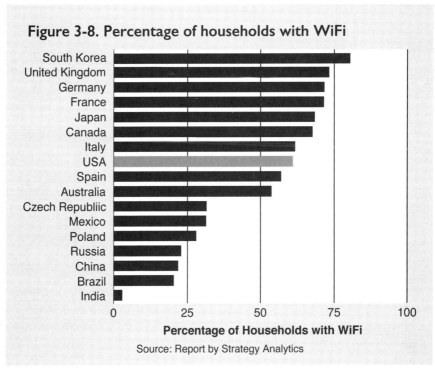

Source: Report by Strategy Analytics

## Smart Appliances

Appliances equipped with Wi-Fi capability are available. Smart clothes dryers turn themselves off when electricity prices are high (or they can be turned off by the EMS). Smart water heaters like the GE GeoSpring Hybrid adjust not only when they heat but how they heat. They can heat water using a high-efficiency heat pump or by using direct-resistance heat. The objective of the control strategy is to maintain user comfort at the lowest cost. Water heaters can also be controlled. These devices sport leading-edge technologies, including the ability to communicate wirelessly with other devices throughout the home and over the Web.

Smart appliance manufacturers see tremendous economic opportunities in directly communicating not only with appliances in the field but also with the users of those appliances. Services such as remote diagnostics and firmware upgrades can be made without user intervention.

Manufacturers are able to bring wirelessly enabled smart appliances quickly to the marketplace by integrating two key building blocks into their products: wireless technology and advanced microcontrollers.

## Summary

Homes can now be equipped with everything they need to make them "smart" (see Figure 3-9). We have smart meters, energy management systems, Wi-Fi, and smart appliances. These devices are linked via Internet connections between the home and the outside world.

In addition, commercial buildings, and factories are ready for TE. We have all the connections necessary to apply the TE model across the electricity ecosystem. By 2020 the Internet connection between the TE Platforms and every device will be virtually complete.

Connection allows remote monitoring and control of energy systems and enables informed long- and short-term decision-making. Producers and consumers can transact directly as well.

Smart meters will remain in place. Where they have not been installed, we can use wireless and Internet-connected devices to measure consumption and communicate with the system.

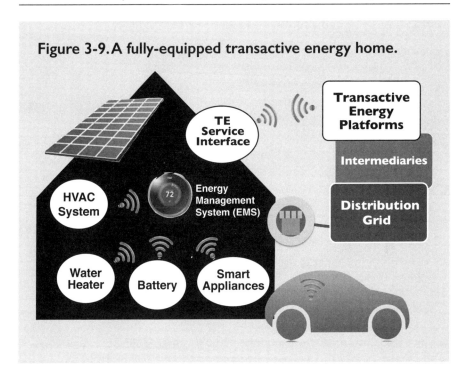

Figure 3-9. A fully-equipped transactive energy home.

# Protocols

## Overview

1. Standardization is necessary in any high-volume, high-speed market like electricity.

2. Protocols define what is transacted and the transaction process, (the nouns and the verbs).

3. TeMix is the approved standard protocol for Transactive Energy.

4. The TeMix interoperation and information models define the processes and the standards for pairwise interactions among parties using simple tenders and transactions.

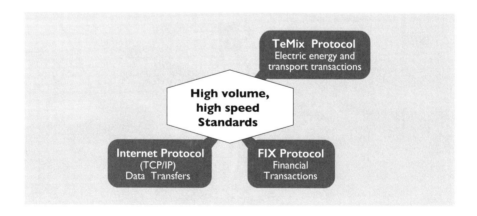

## Standards and protocols support commerce.

The Internet protocol (TCP/IP) is an example of a simple standard that supports high-speed data transfers. The standard has enabled amazing global communication, information access and search, social networks and e-commerce. Businesses such as Google, Apple, Facebook, Amazon, and LinkedIn are built on the foundation of this standard protocol.

The Financial Information eXchange (FIX) protocol is an electronic communications protocol initiated in 1992 for international real-time exchange of information related to the securities transactions and markets with trillions of dollars transacted annually.

The Transactive Energy Market Information Exchange (TeMix) protocol is a standard model for defining tenders and transactions for electricity, together with ways of communicating these messages using other standards such as the Internet protocol.

Standardization is necessary in any commodity market. We measure gasoline in gallons or barrels. We measure corn by the bushel. Electric energy is measured in kilowatt-hours for retail electricity customers.

Generally, it is necessary to standardize on the amount, time of delivery, place of delivery, and quality of the commodity. For example, in the oil market, futures are traded for a kind of oil, a time, and a place, such as barrels of low-sulfur crude oil, delivered 12 months from now, at a terminal in Houston, Texas.

Protocols also define the processes by which trade is conducted. Tendering, transacting, and delivering are processes associated with Transactive Energy (TE).

## Who Sets Standards and Protocols for the Grid?

Several industry groups have established standards for electric energy generation, transmission, distribution, and consumption. Participants in the electric energy ecosystem follow these standards and protocols. One group that oversees electricity markets is the American National Standards Institute (ANSI).

ANSI is the voice of the U.S. standards and conformity assessment system. ANSI empowers its members and constituents to strengthen the U.S. position in the global economy while helping to assure the safety and health of consumers and the protection of the environment.

The Institute oversees the creation, promulgation, and use of thousands of norms and guidelines that directly impact businesses in nearly every sector: acoustical devices, construction equipment, dairy and livestock production, energy distribution, and many more. ANSI also actively engaged in accrediting programs that assess conformance to standards, including globally recognized cross-sector programs such as the ISO 9,000 (quality) and ISO 14,000 (environmental) management systems.

The Organization for the Advancement of Structured Information Standards (OASIS) is a not-for-profit, international consortium that drives the development, convergence, and adoption of open standards for the global information society. OASIS promotes industry consensus and produces worldwide standards for security, privacy, Cloud computing, content technologies, business transactions, energy, emergency management, and other areas. OASIS open standards offer the potential to lower cost, stimulate innovation, grow global markets, and protect the right of free choice of technology. OASIS members broadly represent the marketplace of public and private sector technology leaders, users, and influencers. The consortium has more than 5,000 participants representing over 600 organizations and individual members in 100 countries.

Standards developed by OASIS and ratified by ANSI are eligible for American National Standards designation. "ANSI Accredited Standards Developer status is especially important for standards that will be referenced by national or local policy in the United States or whose stakeholders include government agencies or other groups that demand the highest degree of process assurance" (see *https://www.oasis-open.org/news/pr/oasis-receives-ansi-accreditation*).

In 2009 the Smart Grid Interoperability Panel (SGIP) tasked OASIS to develop standards for the communication of prices and the interoperation among devices and parties on the grid.

## What Is the Smart Grid Interoperability Panel?

The Smart Grid Interoperability Panel (SGIP) was established to support the National Institute for Standards and Technology (NIST) in its fulfillment of its responsibilities pursuant to the Energy Independence and Security Act of 2007.

The SGIP and OASIS created two standards development technical committees: Energy Interoperation (EI) and Energy Market Information Exchange (EMIX). After an extensive review and approval process by OASIS and SGIP, these published standards were entered into the SGIP Catalog of Standards Information Library under the heading "OASIS series."

Two profiles (subsets) of the EI and EMIX standards are specified in the two standards. One is the profile for open automated demand response (OPENADR), and the other is a simplified profile for automation of transactive energy called Transactive Energy Market Information eXchange (TeMix) (see Figure 3-10.)

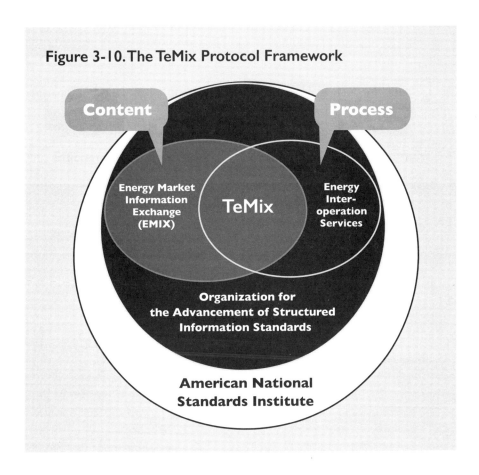

**Figure 3-10. The TeMix Protocol Framework**

## Use of the TeMix Protocol

Those parties or groups that use the TeMix protocol to transact across the electric energy system include the following:

• Energy services: owners of generation, storage, or end devices.
• Transport services: suppliers and consumers of physical energy transport services.
• Intermediaries: parties with no intention of delivery.

Parties that produce, consume, or transport energy interact with the TE Platform through a TE service interface that uses the TeMix protocol. Energy and transport services control their own devices and systems directly but communicate energy tenders and transactions (see Figure 3-11) using the TeMix protocol. Intermediaries communicate directly with the TE Platform using the TeMix protocol.

TeMix needs no hierarchy. Where regulations permit, any party can transact with any other willing party, or with willing intermediaries. No control over another party is implied except as mutually agreed in a transaction. Options may be transacted for risk management or reliability reasons.

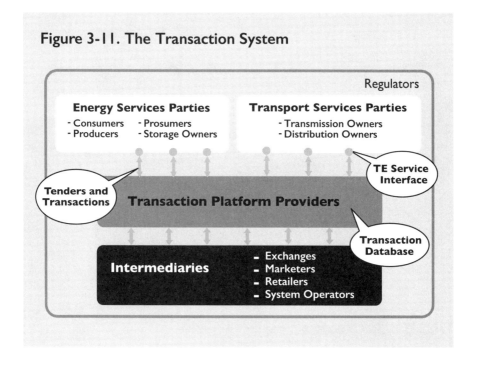

## Figure 3-11. The Transaction System

## TeMix Products

TeMix products are a subset or profile of EMIX power products (see Figure 3-10). The TeMix products are based on blocks of energy and transport. Energy is scheduled at a constant rate (power level) over a delivery interval. Each transaction imposes an obligation on the buy side to purchase and on the sell side to deliver energy. The two TeMix products are energy and transport.

Time and power measures are particularly important with electric energy because it is delivered at the speed of light and measured precisely. (TE can support both real and reactive energy transactions, if necessary.) Other energy forms like oil are delivered over periods of days or months and they are measured in barrels or tankers.

The delivery interval is specified by start date and time, and duration. Delivery intervals are nested so shorter intervals fit within longer duration intervals. For example, a calendar year is divided into calendar months, days, hours, 5-minute or 4-second intervals.

## TeMix Processes

The TeMix protocol supports decentralized decision-making and coordination using near-continuous, asynchronous communications of tenders among parties.

The TeMix market process is characterized by transactive states. TeMix uses the following five transactive states:

1) **Indication of interest**. An indication of interest is nonbinding and nonactionable. It is (a) a request for a tender, (b) a forecast of usage or supply, or (c) a forecast of price. An indication of interest together with a price is commonly called a "quote."

2) **Tender**. A tender is a price and quantity for a transaction with an expiration date time. The side of the tender is buy or sell.

3) **Transaction**. A transaction is formed by accepting a tender.

4) **Position**. A position is the result of several transactions.

5) **Delivery**. A delivery is the metered quantity delivered usually offset by a position resulting from several transactions.

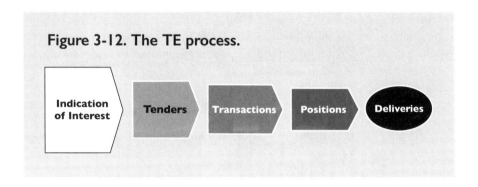

## Figure 3-12. The TE process.

Indication of Interest → Tenders → Transactions → Positions → Deliveries

## Transactions Are Associated with a Physical Place

At some point, the transaction world has to connect unambiguously with the physical world. We have to specify a place where electricity is put into the system or taken out.

A transaction for energy, therefore, has to occur at a place or location on the grid. For example, the transaction may be at the end of a transmission line somewhere in the Rocky Mountains or at a substation on the outskirts of Chicago. It is like ordering a book from Amazon. There is the address where the books are to be delivered and place where they are stored in an Amazon warehouse.

The interface is either an End Device or a Node (see Table 3-2). A Master Resource ID (MRID) uniquely identifies a physical device. A node is a place in the physical transport network, such as the location of a generator, or a substation at the end of a transmission line.

EMIX defines more complex interfaces in terms of the MRID and node concepts. For example, a "transport interface" is a segment of a transmission network as specified by two nodes: a point of receipt and a point of delivery (see Table 3-2).

| Table 3-2. Emix interface descriptions | |
|---|---|
| **EMIX POWER INTERFACE** | **DESCRIPTION** |
| Service Area | Locations or regions relevant to power transactions. |
| End Device Asset | Physical device (MRID). |
| Meter Asset | Physical device or devices that perform the role of the meter (MRID). |
| Pricing (PNode) | Location in an ISO/RTO where participants submit bids and the ISO/RTO publishes locational prices. |
| Aggregated Pricing Node | Specialized type of pricing node for zone, control area, or aggregated generation, load, or trading hub. |
| Service Location | Location where ownership of service changes hands,. Potentially has many service delivery points. |
| Service DeliveryPoint | Logical point where ownership of service changes. |
| Transport Interface | Delineates edges at ends of a transport segment. Names two nodes: point of receipt and point of delivery. |

## Communication of Tenders and Transactions

TE tenders and transactions are communicated using the TeMix protocol. There are two parts to the protocol:

1. "Web services" that communicate tenders and transactions from a party to a TE Platform.

2. "Payload" that describes the parameters of the tender or transaction communicated by the Web service.

TeMix Web services are used by software applications to create new tenders and transactions, and to request information on existing tenders and transactions.

The four key TeMix Web services defined by the OASIS Energy Interoperation (EI) Standard are:

- EiCreateTender
- EiRequestTender
- EiCreate Transaction
- EiRequest Transaction

Each of these services communicates a payload containing the TeMix Elements (see Table 3-3). Additional elements describing units and currency are communicated by the market context the communication.

| Table 3-3. Temix payload elements | |
| --- | --- |
| **ELEMENT** | **DESCRIPTION** |
| Power Product | Energy or transport. |
| Start Date Time | When the interval begins. |
| Duration | Extent of time interval. |
| Price | Unit energy price. |
| Power Quantity | Rate of delivery of energy over interval |
| Side | Buy or sell. |
| Expires | Time tender expires. |
| EMIX Interface | One node for energy. Two nodes for transport. |

The basic TE communication is initiated when a party creates a tender using EiCreateTender and the tender is accepted by another party by using EiCreateTransaction.

## The Interface between Device and Systems and Tenders and Transaction

There is a TE service interface that implements the TeMix protocol between every physical device or system and the retail or wholesale tenders and transactions. It doesn't matter conceptually whether the "device" is a 1,000 MW coal-fired power plant, a smart home, or a single electric car. (see Figure 3-13).

Typically, a device is being managed by a management algorithm. Homes have energy management systems (EMSs). Wind farms have sophisticated algorithms that take weather forecasts and local wind conditions and use the information to trim the blades on the turbines. Battery storage devices will have controllers that manage charge rates, discharge rates, and depth of discharge.

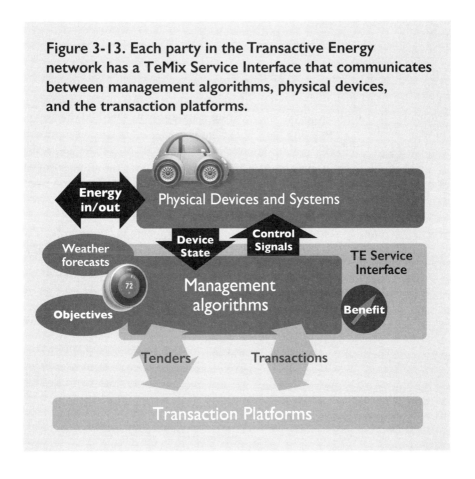

**Figure 3-13. Each party in the Transactive Energy network has a TeMix Service Interface that communicates between management algorithms, physical devices, and the transaction platforms.**

The management algorithms will also accept tenders from other parties to consummate transactions or they may post tenders that others may accept using TE Platforms. These transactions will be done in a way that maximizes profit or benefit based on the device owner's objectives. The EMS is acting as the "agent" of the building owner.

The management algorithm can also interact with a variety of external information sources like weather reports, traffic reports, and an owner global positioning system (GPS). The tremendous potential for improving overall electric system efficiency results from the combination of information gathering and optimization.

The TE service interface is an information standard that may be implemented in software or hardware such as a chip embedded in an EMS. It is programmed to use the TeMix protocol.

## Summary

All the necessary protocols are in place to implement the TE model. The TeMix protocol is the combination of two existing standards: the OASIS EMIX Information model for content and the OASIS Energy Interoperation services model for process. The TeMix standards are open and free to all. All parties can communicate tenders and transactions with each other while maintaining control of their own devices and systems. The TeMix protocols enable automation of TE, which makes the benefits of TE widely accessible.

The benefits of this protocol result from its simplicity. Similar to the Internet economy and financial transactions that are built on simple communication protocols, the TE business model will be built on the simple TeMix protocols.

CHAPTER 4

# The Challenges and Opportunities We Face

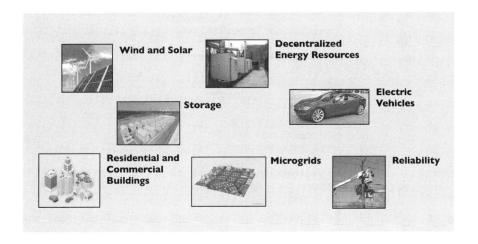

The changes in energy markets are creating significant challenges to integration of wind and solar, decentralized storage, decentralized energy resources (DERs), microgrids, the operation of home, buildings, and industry, along with capitalizing on the emergence of the electric vehicle. We describe these challenges in this chapter and explain how the Transactive Energy business model can meet the challenges.

Over half of the states have Renewable Portfolio Standard Policies. These policies are a commitment to obtain a certain percentage of energy from renewable energy by a specified date. California has committed to produce 33% of its electrical energy from renewables by 2020. These targets do not include customer-owned renewables such as rooftop solar.

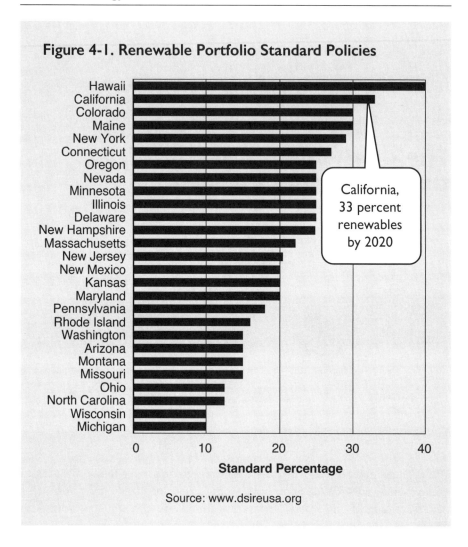

Figure 4-1. Renewable Portfolio Standard Policies

Source: www.dsireusa.org

Most renewable energy will come from centralized and decentralized solar and wind. Figure 4-1 shows the percentage of these policy standards for 28 states. California is near the top with 33%. Texas has a capacity standard. Internationally, Germany has a renewables goal of 40%–45% by 2025 and 55%–60% by 2035.

The shift to renewables has increased the need for storage technologies. Wind is available only when the wind blows. Solar is only available when the sun shines. We need a system that responds to this variability and moves usage toward periods when low-cost wind and solar are available. Storage is one way to do this. California has mandated the deployment of 1,325 megawatts (MW) of grid energy storage by 2020.

The focus on renewables and efficiency has spurred the deployment of decentralized generation. Lower cost PV panels and customer incentives have resulted in a boom in decentralized solar. Incentives and technology have also resulted in rapid installations of cogeneration facilities. These technologies have the advantage that they are located close to customers. They lower the need for transmission and distribution facilities and reduce energy losses.

Microgrids are springing up like mushrooms. The motivations are mixed. The University of California, San Diego, is creating a microgrid because they believe they can lower total energy costs by planning a stand-alone integrated system. Apple's new campus in Cupertino, California, will be a microgrid, so that in a grid outage Apple's valuable employees and equipment can continue to be productive. Military installations are creating microgrids to lower costs and improve energy security and resilience. Bases can't afford to be vulnerable to grid-wide blackouts or natural disasters. In 2012 Hurricane Sandy along the east coast of the United States demonstrated our vulnerability to the loss of the grid.

Decentralized generation and microgrids are creating concerns for investor-owned utilities (IOUs). It is easy to imagine a scenario where a large share of the customers have migrated off the grid and a handful of customers are left with the bill for the transmission and distribution system.

The electric vehicle will add new demand to the system and it will change load shapes. Electric vehicles offer the flexibility of storage as a by-product. We can charge or discharge the vehicle batteries in any pattern as long as the energy is there when needed for transportation. The average American home uses about 30 kilowatt-hours (kWh) of electric energy per day. A Tesla car battery stores about 50 kWh and a Nissan Leaf about 20 kWh. This means that the battery in an electric car will probably be able to supply a household's energy needs for a day. This will figure into reliability considerations.

These changes are making investment and operating decisions more complex. How do we coordinate producer and customer investments? How do we coordinate producer and customer operating decisions?

All these developments mean that the electric power system is poised for big changes in the next 10 to 30 years. They would be intimidating were it not for developments in technology and the promise of innovation.

In the following sections we will connect TE with these developments: renewables, the need for building efficiency, decentralized energy resources, microgrids, and the electric vehicle.

SECTION I

# Integrating Wind and solar

## Overview

TE facilitates the growth of wind and solar by:

1. Reducing investment risk.
2. Moving electricity usage toward times when wind and solar are available.
3. Making it easy for PV panel owners to sell energy.

The Transactive Energy model facilitates the growth of wind and solar in many ways. First, it reduces the investment risk. Second, it moves usage toward times when the wind blows and the sun shines. TE also facilitates storage. Storage can capture wind and solar energy and move it to other time periods.

This makes solar and wind more attractive. TE tender prices also help consumers save money by helping them use more energy when solar and wind are available and less when they are not available.

Wind power tends to be concentrated in remote areas. This means power must be transmitted long distances to users. PV panels are scattered throughout the network. Most are on building rooftops. TE takes these location factors into account by separating the price of energy and transport.

The California Independent System Operator (ISO) has carried out studies of the impact of wind and especially solar on the grid. If estimates of production from wind and solar are subtracted from total demand, such as in the evening when the sun sets, the resulting "net load" looks like the "duck curve" (see Figure 4-2). The "duck"-shaped curve is the energy load that typically is served with conventional sources such as fossil fueled generators.

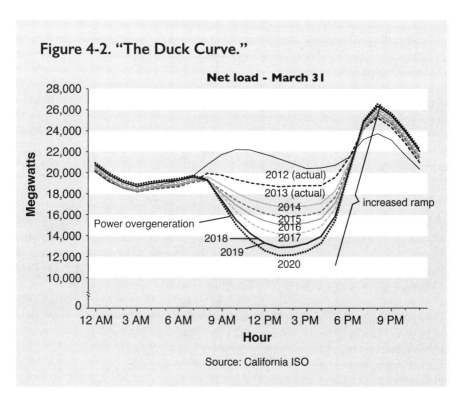

Figure 4-2. "The Duck Curve."

There are two interesting things about this curve. First, there is an increasingly large ramp in net load as the solar drops off in the late afternoon and the evening residential load increases. By 2020 the ramp is shown to be more than 13,000 MW in about 3 hours on some days. This is beyond the limits of the current system.

The second interesting thing is that the net load is very low in the middle of the day because of increasing solar generation. This is below the minimum output of conventional resources. If that is the case then we will be in a situation where we have "too much" generation and some energy might have to be wasted.

Duck curves are already apparent in California, Hawaii, Germany, and other systems with significant amounts of solar—and these curves change every day.

The message from this simplistic analysis is that we will need sources of flexibility to adjust demand curves. The flexibility can come from end-use modification, storage, or decentralized generation not ordinarily dispatched by the California ISO. The TE model is ideal for mobilizing these resources when they are needed.

Solar and wind investors face a situation that is different from investors in a conventional generation unit. A conventional generation unit can maximize profit by operating when it is profitable to do so. Wind and solar projects cannot do this. They are "on" when the wind blows or the sun shines, "off" when mother nature decides to turn them off, and their generation can change rapidly. This variability or lack of predictability places a premium on forward transactions.

Forward TE subscription transactions can fix the renewable operator's revenues. This will lower risk and financing costs for wind and solar projects. Forward TE transactions take the place of the power purchase agreements many wind and solar developers use today. With TE subscriptions, these projects can sell subscriptions directly to end-use customers. In fact, at least one solar provider, SolarCity, is already offering homeowners subscriptions for rooftop installations.

With the TE model in place, all wind and solar projects will be able to sell subscriptions (forward contracts) at fixed annual costs for several years for a specified percentage of the actual output of a project. Output can be measured in small intervals such as an hour, 5 minutes, or 4 seconds, depending on metering and local market conventions. The subscriptions will deliver a prescribed share of the actual output of a wind or solar project or a group of projects to the buyer.

## TE Moves Usage toward Wind and Solar

We want to move electric energy usage to periods of high supply and low usage from periods of high usage and low supply. Historically, the latter has been on hot summer days when air conditioning use is high.

Solar power is available during the sunny, hot part of the day. It coincides with the air conditioning load. The availability of cheap solar power may move the peak load period away from the historic hot day the California ISO predicts for California. But we do not know exactly when there will be surplus or deficits of energy.

Because wind and solar have almost no operating cost, the prices for this energy will no longer be based on only generator operating cost. Prices will be based on customer willingness to pay as a function of their need and the supply they are tendered. The prices will change from minute to minute, hour-to-hour, day-to-day, season-to-season, and region-to-region.

In the future we want a business model where prices are determined by the supply and demand of willing parties. A model where equilibrium prices balance variable supply and variable demand. This is what TE does. It does this without intervention. It will be futile in the future to try to define "peak" periods and "off" peak periods. The lows and highs will continually shift with the sun and the wind. Likewise, it will be impossible to set spot prices in advance or to limit the variability of spot prices without wasting renewable energy or imposing shortages on consumers.

## TE Facilitates Storage

Renewables and storage have a strong synergy. Wind often blows at night and the sun shines on solar panels in the middle of the day. Storage is a way of moving the low-cost energy from wind and solar to times of the day when system demands are high or energy is especially valuable.

Nighttime is also when electric vehicles are tucked away in their garages. The energy management systems on vehicles will be able to capture the low-cost wind energy by using it to charge batteries. In addition, when excess solar is available in the middle of the day it can be used to charge parked electric vehicles.

## TE Promotes Efficiency in Transmission and Distribution

Most solar power will be generated by PV panels located close to where the energy is used. This is an advantage because it will lower transmission and distribution costs.

In general, customers with PV panels will lower the need for transport. They will need to pay for some transport during periods when they are net importers of energy. They will also pay for transport when they are delivering excess energy into the grid. The spot transport prices in each direction will depend on the flow in relation to the transport network capacity and the need to recover more fixed transport costs during times of heavy transport usage.

The TE model makes it simple to account for the use of transmission and distribution by PV panel owners. The forward and spot tenders and transactions will reflect the costs of the two-way transport service. This is an advantage of separating transport and energy.

Wind farms, on the other hand, tend to be located in remote areas. The energy is generated far from urban areas where demand for electricity is concentrated. Figure 4-3 shows the anticipated concentration of wind generation facilities in the western United States.

The locational disadvantage is accounted for in the TE model. Forward tenders for transport from the wind facilities will include the cost of building transmission lines. Spot tenders will reflect the cost of moving the energy long distances where there may be congestion and higher incremental energy losses.

TE coordinates the locational factors in a way that promotes efficiency and fairness. Consumers pay for energy and transport services separately. Sources in remote sites will be penalized, whereas production close to consumers will be rewarded.

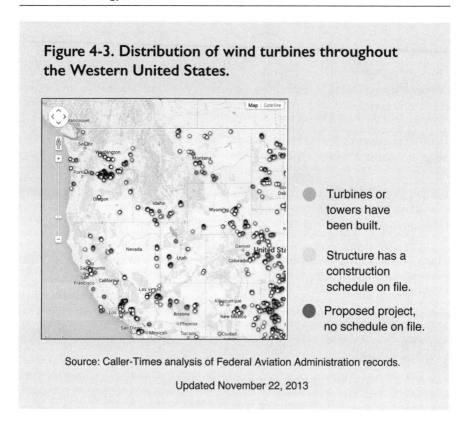

Figure 4-3. Distribution of wind turbines throughout the Western United States.

Turbines or towers have been built.

Structure has a construction schedule on file.

Proposed project, no schedule on file.

Source: Caller-Times analysis of Federal Aviation Administration records.

Updated November 22, 2013

## Summary

TE will promote efficient wind and solar projects by lowering risk and moving energy demand toward periods when they are producing. TE will facilitate the synergy between solar and storage. Finally, TE gives us a way to account for the locational advantages and disadvantages of solar and wind, respectively.

SECTION 2

# Integrating Storage

## Overview

1. Storage is used to move energy from one time period to another.

2. The need for storage is increasing.

3. Storage comes in many forms:

- pumped hydro
- large batteries
- thermal
- compressed air
- electric vehicle batteries

4. Storage can be placed almost anywhere in the electric power ecosystem.

5. TE promotes efficient storage investment and operating decisions.

Transactive Energy (TE) supports the efficient use of storage throughout the grid. Storage is needed so that cheaper energy is available at peak times when it can be more expensive. Most storage is relatively expensive to install; however, the cost of storage is dropping rapidly.

The TE business model provides storage investors with the information they need to make sound decisions. Storage investors can use forward transactions to reduce the financial risks of high storage investments.

The round trip efficiency of storage devices is from 70% to 90% for each kWh of energy put in. TE forward tender prices provide the information necessary to decide when to charge and when to discharge storage.

In Japan, 15% of the electrical energy consumed has been stored. In the U.S., grid-scale storage is less than 2%. The California state legislature has set targets of 1,325 megawatts (MW) by 2020 for new storage installation for the three investor-owned utilities (IOUs). Installed storage capacity in the United States is currently about 22,000 MW. Most of this is pumped hydro.

### Figure 4-4. Common grid storage technologies.

Typical Pumped Hydro Plant Arrangement. The Helms Hydro Station in California is 1,200 MW, and an estimated 12,000 MWh.

Sodium Sulfur Storage 34MW, 250 MWh, (Source: NGK Inc. Rokkasho Japan, 2008)

Electric vehicle, 2 to 20 kW, 10 to 85 kWh.

## Storage Technology

Historically, most storage has been pumped hydro (see Figure 4-4). Water is pumped uphill when power is cheap and it is run downhill through turbines when power is needed. For example, the Swiss buy excess nuclear energy from France at night and use it to pump water up into mountain reservoirs. The energy is used to serve Swiss customers during daytime hours of high demand.

The Energy Storage Association (*www.energystorage.org*) defines six main categories of energy storage:

**Solid state batteries**—a range of electrochemical storage solutions including advanced chemistry batteries and capacitors.

**Flow batteries**—batteries where energy is stored directly in an electrolyte solution for longer life and quick response times.

**Flywheels**—mechanical devices that harness rotational energy to deliver instantaneous energy.

**Compressed air energy storage**—utilizing compressed air to create an energy reserve.

**Thermal**—capturing heat and cold to create energy on demand.

**Pumped hydro-power**—creating large-scale reservoirs of energy with water.

Size and weight are not nearly as important in grid applications as they are for electric vehicle applications. The key components of grid use are efficiency and cost.

## Transmission and Distribution Advantages of Storage

A key advantage of some types of storage is site flexibility. A battery can be placed almost anywhere there is enough space. This means that it can be placed in the transmission and distribution system where it is most beneficial for efficiency and reliability. Pumped hydro storage has to be sited where there is a vertical drop for water. A lead acid battery can be placed virtually anywhere, including a homeowners basement.

Locating storage at or close to the customers can reduce the need for new investment in distribution and transmission. And the operation of storage close to the load can reduce losses on the transmission and distribution grid.

Prosumers with PV panels in California recently began installing batteries in their homes to back up their solar systems. This not only offered reliability but also profitability. They could charge the batteries from the grid off-peak and sell the energy into the grid on-peak for a profit. Southern California Edison cried foul. The on-/off-peak rates for Net Metering customers were approved by the California Public Utility Commission to promote solar, not to incentivize batteries. The incentive for batteries was an unintended consequence even though most agreed that storage could reduce the impact on the grid of customer-owned solar.

In the TE model the situation in Southern California would not be an issue. Storage owned by consumers is treated exactly the same as storage owned by the utility. The TE business model properly prices two-way flows of energy and transport while it recovers the investments in transport by the utilities. Storage will tend to be located where it is most beneficial to the system and the most profitable to the owner.

## Operation of Storage Using Forward Tenders

We can illustrate the TE operation of storage with an example of a stand-alone battery system at a substation at the distribution/transmission grid interface. The battery has an automated energy management system (EMS.) The EMS communicates with the battery control system and with one or more TE Platforms using TE tenders and transactions.

From time to time, the battery EMS automatically receives buy-and-sell tenders from the TE Platform for the next 24-hour window. It receives 96 (or 24 x 4), 15-minute buy tenders for energy delivered to the substation and 96, 15-minute sell tenders for energy delivered from the substation.

If in any interval there are energy tenders from more than one counter party, perhaps on the same or different TE Platforms, then the EMS can work with the best tenders in each interval. The best buy tender is the lowest-priced buy tender and the best sell tender is the highest-priced sell tender.

The EMS searches for high-priced, 15-minute intervals where it can increase the amount sold from discharging without exceeding the minimum storage capacity; it also searches for low-priced, 15-minute intervals where it can increase the amount bought for charging without exceeding the maximum energy storage capacity of the battery.

This search process is set up as an automated mathematical algorithm that maximizes the profit to the battery owner while considering the current state of charge, battery temperature, and all of the nonlinear characteristics and constraints of the specific battery chemistry and physics and power conversion from alternative current to direct current and back to alternating current.

When the calculations are done the EMS then accepts tenders as transactions that will improve the profit to the owner of the battery. This locks in the profit for the owner.

As the day proceeds, conditions on the grid change. Suppose there is suddenly a surplus of wind or solar. As a result tenders for buying and selling will change. Wind producers will be offering to sell energy at very low prices. The storage EMS will update its projections and reallocate purchases and sales if possible within the operational constraints of the battery. This process is repeated continuously throughout the day.

This TE operation of storage will work the same way for millions of storage devices of any type located anywhere on the grid (behind the customer meter, on the distribution grid or on the transmission grid). No central operator needs to know the current state of charge or detailed characteristic of each of the millions of storage devices. The TE interactions of buyers and sellers of energy and transport will make the best use of all storage. Storage will facilitate integration of renewables, reduce the customer costs, and assure reliable service.

## Summary

The TE model provides incentives for effective storage investment and operation. It also provides incentives to innovate. The advantage of the TE model for storage investors is that forward price and quantity buy-and-sell information is available.

Spot prices enable the storage operators to continuously optimize the storage operation to maximize profit. EMS systems will be designed to account for the nonlinear constraints and physics of the specific storage technologies and designs.

Another advantage is that TE separates energy and transport products. This allows investors and operators to take advantage of site flexibility offered by storage technologies. Storage will be operated to manage both energy and transport on the grid at a profit.

Storage will play an increasingly larger role in the electrical system. The TE business model will be an enabler of a future where more storage is used and it is located in the right places.

SECTION 3

# Integrating Homes and Commercial Buildings

## Overview

1. Most fossil fuels reduction and cost savings will come from efficiency improvements in buildings.

2. Heating and cooling demands are primary contributors.

3. Customer investments are smarter and less risky with the TE model.

   • Forward transactions coordinate investment decisions.
   • Spot transactions coordinate operating decisions.

4. All customers and producers do business on a level playing field.

5. Customers act autonomously.

According to the Rocky Mountain Institute (RMI), it is feasible and economic to phase out oil, coal, and nuclear energy by 2050. The net savings in total energy costs would be in the neighborhood of about $5 trillion net present value (NPV) (see "Reinventing Fire" by Amory Lovins).

A big part of the gains projected by RMI will come from reductions in electricity use in residential and commercial buildings. Electricity is a good place to look for fossil fuels reductions because for every kWh of electric energy saved we save about three kWh of fuel energy. (The savings range from zero for renewables to as high as five for old gas-fired plants.) We also save the energy lost in transmission and distribution. This averages about 7% of generation. The incremental losses can be three to four times larger at times of peak demand.

Realizing the potential efficiency gains will require large investments by millions of homeowners and business people. Government intervention has been helpful to stimulate investment in new technology and reduce the risks to early adopters. Ultimately, we want these investments to be guided by commercial markets.

## Customer Investments Will Be Smarter and Less Risky with the TE Model

The TE model offers residential and commercial customers the same sophisticated decision-making tools that large wholesale customers have today. A homeowner will be able to do financial evaluations for any investment in a new appliance or home energy project using logic that is easily embedded in a smartphone. A smartphone working together with an EMS is able to do the following:

• Estimate future kWh usage and hourly patterns.
• Access the manufacturer's information on appliance costs and operating characteristics.
• Access energy and transport tenders on TE Platforms.
• All customers, large and small, will be able to go to the TE Platform and retrieve firm forward-priced tenders for electricity for several years in advance.
• Estimate future cash flows and calculate NPV and paybacks.
• Show comparisons.

Customers will be able to lock in energy savings using forward transactions (subscriptions.) They will be able to do this for their entire home or for single devices, such as solar panels or batteries.

Residential and commercial customers will use subscriptions to reduce the risk of future operating costs exceeding their estimates. This will make efficiency investments much easier than today.

There is little doubt that better information and risk reduction will steer more buyers toward more efficient and practical choices. Today, the buyer of a new refrigerator must rely on a government mandated efficiency sticker on the appliance at the store. The efficiency ratings are ambiguous and the estimates of savings are based on average usage and electricity prices. It is a "buyer beware" situation. Your situation may differ greatly from the "average" customer.

The TE model will stimulate investment in new technology by reducing consumer risk. Forward transactions give homeowners and small businesses access to the same risk management mechanisms that huge wholesale customers use.

## Coordination of Investments

Coordination of investments is the big challenge faced by today's electric power system planners. How do we decide whether to invest in responsive "smart" appliances and HVAC (heating, ventilation, and air conditioning) to reduce peak demand or install new combustion turbines? Do we invest in many small batteries in homeowner's basements or fewer large storage units? How much wind and solar power is optimal? These are impossible questions for planners to answer because of the complexity of the systems, the different objectives of stakeholders, and all the uncertainties we face.

Planners are deluding themselves if they think they can develop a framework for centrally designing the optimal system. It is simply an impossible task. Today, planners are really only coordinating central producers. They will never be able to coordinate investment across the whole electricity ecosystem.

The TE model uses forward transactions to coordinate investment decisions across the ecosystem. The coordination mechanism is simple. All parties have access to the same TE Platforms where all producer and consumer tenders are posted. A homeowner sees the same tenders that an industrial customer sees. A customer can analyze an investment in PV panels or small storage using the same market projections that a combustion turbine investor uses.

It is the coordination capability of the TE model that offers the promise of making smarter efficiency investments throughout the system. The energy system will be constantly improving itself as long as individual customers, large and small, have access to the TE Platform and they have sophisticated energy management systems. Capital will migrate naturally to the most "profitable" investments independent of technology or ownership.

## Customers Will Make Smarter Operating Decisions

It makes no sense to invest in a smart appliance and then operate it in a dumb way. Attaining the world's potential efficiency gains will require the smart operation of devices like heaters, air conditioners, and a plethora of appliances.

The TE model uses spot transactions to coordinate operating decisions. The spot tenders for all energy buyers and sellers are available on the TE Platforms in, for instance, 15-minute time intervals.

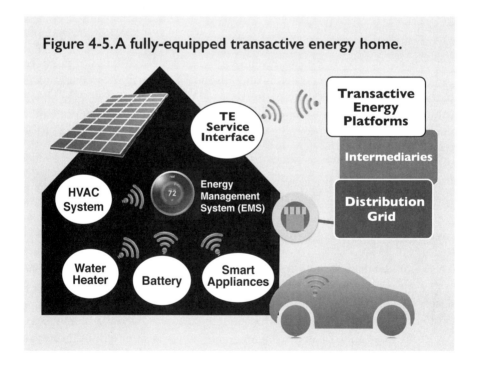

Figure 4-5. A fully-equipped transactive energy home.

We can illustrate how the TE model works for a home with an HVAC system, solar panels, a battery, and appliances. Our sample home has an automated energy management system (EMS.) The EMS communicates with the appliances—including devices like air conditioners, refrigerators, clothes dryers, and swimming pool pumps. Inside the home the EMS also communicates with the solar panels and the battery (see Figure 4-5).

Outside of the home the EMS communicates with a TE Platform that is probably hosted on "Cloud" computers. The EMS also has access to weather forecasts and the usage patterns of the home's occupants.

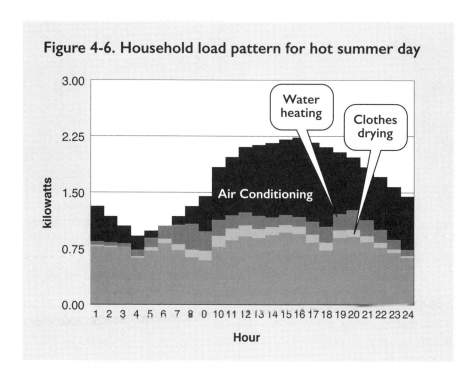

Figure 4-6. Household load pattern for hot summer day

The household energy planning process begins when the EMS makes a projection of the net usage of the home for the next 24 hours (see Figure 4-6). The projection accounts for owner habits, current schedule and the use of devices like the HVAC system, clothes dryer, and water heater.

Next the EMS looks at the local weather forecast and estimates the output of the PV panels (see Figure 4-7). The solar panel output peaks at about noon or a little later if the panels face west. This happens to be close to the peak time for the household load shown in Figure 4-6. This should be no surprise. The household peak is determined by the air conditioning demand. (Air conditioning load usually lags the solar energy input and often carries over into the evening if the home is not occupied during the day.) In this case the sun is driving both the demand for air conditioning and the supply from the PV panels.

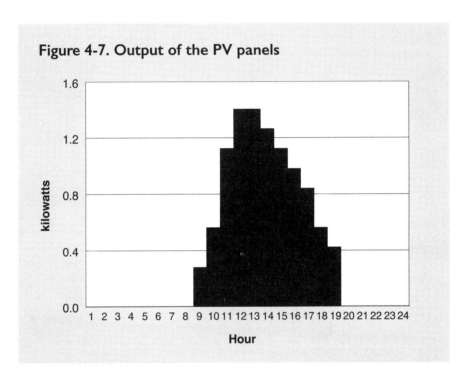

## Figure 4-7. Output of the PV panels

Now that the EMS has estimates of household needs and solar energy it will be active on the TE Platform buying and selling energy for the day. The first step is to sum up all the deliveries or sales it has already transacted (subscribed) for. The household will have subscribed to buy or sell certain amounts of energy hour by hour. This is called a "position."

The combination of the household demands and subscriptions is shown in Figure 4-8. The gray area is the difference between subscriptions and total demand.

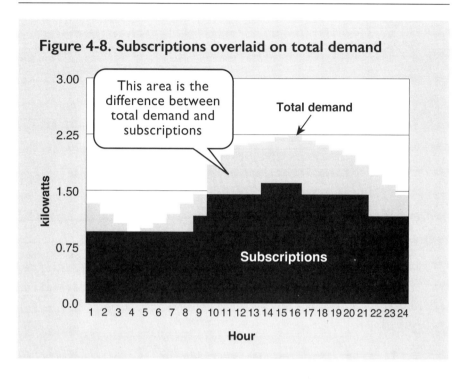

Figure 4-8. Subscriptions overlaid on total demand

The EMS system can now combine the demand, subscriptions, and PV panel output to see net energy needs. The result is shown in Figure 4-9. It appears that there will be an excess of energy midday. This energy can be stored or sold. Later in the day there is a shortfall. This energy can be purchased or retrieved from battery storage. The EMS can also control the smart appliances or provide information to the occupants to modify the demand pattern.

At this point the EMS will begin optimizing. It will buy, sell, and store in a way that maximizes net benefit for the homeowner. The EMS influences the control of the smart appliances: the clothes dryer, the air conditioner, and the water heater. These loads are somewhat controllable but controlling them will usually have some impact on building occupants. For example, if the air conditioner is interrupted then it will change room temperatures and comfort levels. The EMS has information on both expected room occupation and homeowner preferences for room comfort. These preferences can be changed by the customer at any time. The EMS uses preference information together with economic information to make appliance operating decisions.

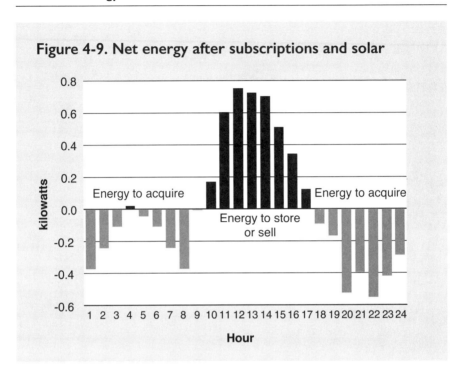

### Figure 4-9. Net energy after subscriptions and solar

The battery is different. It can shift energy from one period to another without impacting household occupants. It can also buy and sell power in a way that maximizes profit for the homeowner. The EMS will account for the fact that the round trip efficiency of the battery is 70% to 90%. The battery in the homeowner's electric vehicle can also be integrated into the system.

The EMS accesses the TE Platform to get economic information. Buy-and-sell tenders for both energy and transport are available on the TE Platforms. A sophisticated algorithm in the EMS will estimate net cost for deliveries to the house and sales for energy from the house based on location.

As the day unfolds, the EMS will monitor the system and make adjustments. Spot transactions will be used to fine tune the system in a way that maximizes homeowner's net benefit.

## Spot Transactions Will Coordinate Building Operating Decisions throughout the Electricity Ecosystem

All residential and commercial buildings have access to the same spot tenders on the TE Platform. The buy-and-sell tenders are essentially spot prices. (The term "tender" implies the buildings can buy or sell up to a given amount at the tendered price; this is different from a forecast of a price that might change and cannot be locked in at the time operating decisions are made.)

Spot tender prices coordinate operating decisions throughout the system. Take a simple decision like, "Should we run a combustion turbine, or discharge energy from storage, or interrupt a customer's air conditioner?" In today's command and control system this is a difficult choice. In the TE model this decision does not have to be made centrally. The storage will operate if it is profitable to do so. The combustion turbine will start if it is profitable. Customers will change their air conditioning use patterns if it is beneficial to them. All the decisions are made autonomously. They are coordinated through the TE Platforms.

As a net result, demands will move toward periods with high production of renewable energy. Demand will move away from periods of low renewables production. The system will move away from any costly peaks that might emerge.

It seems almost too good to be true. Communication and computing technology have improved so fast that it is possible to do things today that were inconceivable just 10 years ago.

Residential and commercial customers have access to the same information as wholesale customers. A single building has access to the same sophisticated decision-making algorithms as huge ISOs and IOUs.

Information and decision-making are in the hands of the customer. This is good because customers are becoming both producers and consumers—"prosumers." TE allows them to be smoothly integrated into the system when and where it is practical. It does not matter whether they are buyers or sellers, or both.

There is no need for subsidies to encourage rational behavior in the TE model. People acting in their own interest do what is best for the system. The system is always moving toward higher system-wide efficiency.

The TE model does not preclude direct-load control by utilities. It offers the promise of delivering the same result with less cost and no intervention.

If, for political reasons, society wants to encourage certain technologies like solar water heating or regional economic development then this can be done within the TE framework. For example, a carbon tax can be levied and enforced within the framework of the TE Platform and intermediaries.

## Summary

The TE model will unleash a torrent of entrepreneurial thinking and activity in the residential and commercial building sector. This is important because these are the sectors we are counting on for major improvements in efficiency and cost.

Subscriptions will permit smarter investment decisions. This will make it easier to upgrade to the next level of building efficiency strategies.

Spot transactions will encourage smarter operating decisions by everyone. All customers and producers interact on a level playing field with a high degree of transparency. Incentives are aligned between IOUs and customers.

SECTION 4

# Integrating Decentralized Energy Resources (DER's)

## Overview

1. **Decentralized Energy Resources (DER's)** are increasing in usage. These include:

- PV solar panels
- cogeneration
- back up power

2. Many of these resources are not completely controllable and they are often coupled with other demands like building heating.

3. TE facilitates the investment and operating decisions for decentralized plants.

4. The TE model enables owners to capture the transmission and distribution benefits of DER.

Traditional forms of decentralized energy resources (DERs) include cogeneration plants powered by waste heat from an industrial process or natural gas. Newer forms include PV panels. Lesser-known DERs are small hydro and cogeneration fueled by landfill gas, biogas, or solar heat. The Rocky Mountain Institute has provided a comprehensive description of what is meant by "decentralized."

> *"When we say "decentralized" we are actually referring to several distinct characteristics of an electrical resource, each important for different purposes. "Decentralized" usually means dispersed geographically and connected to the distribution system rather than the transmission system, so the resources are nearer consumers, saving grid costs and reducing losses and failures. But "decentralized" resources are also often modular—made in small, similar chunks that can be linked together. Modular technologies get their economies from mass production and rapid learning, not unit scale, and they improve reliability by replacing vulnerable big units with a diversified portfolio of many small units that are unlikely to fail all at once. Finally, in some contexts, "decentralized" resources are small, in the kilowatt- to several megawatt range, versus the hundreds or thousands of megawatts produced by a coal or nuclear plant. The smaller scale can save money by better matching most needs. In the mid-1990's, three-fourths of U.S. residential loads didn't exceed roughly 1.5 kW, nor three-fourths of commercial loads 12 kW.*
>
> *Reinventing Fire: Bold Business Solutions for the New Energy Era, Amory Lovins and the Rocky Mountain Institute, Page 206, 2011*

## Decentralized Energy Resources Present Challenges

What makes DER's somewhat problematic for grid planners is that almost all of them are variable. Solar is available when the sun shines. Cogeneration is tied to needs of building and factory operations. Other decentralized generation is subject to the availability of fuel as with biomass or water flow with hydro.

Large centralized energy resources have typically been managed (dispatched) by a local utility or an ISO as elements of a portfolio of generation projects. Centralized resources are generally operated for the single purpose of generating electricity and related service.

Decentralized energy resources often have multiple uses and thus are best managed by coordinated self-dispatch. Electricity generation may be just a by-product. It is difficult for a central operator to gather detailed information on DERs and the preferences of their owners. TE facilitates the coordinated investment and self-dispatch of DER.

The TE business model provides a framework in which effective DER investment and operating decisions can be made autonomously and coordinated with investment and operating decisions of other energy and transport service parties.

Multiyear DER forward transactions can be made based on forward tenders for energy and transport at the location of the DER facility. The considerations will include the following:

• Expected and actual production from the DER.
• Forward tender prices.
• Investment and operating costs.
• Other information specific to the owner's other uses of the DER, such as process heat or pumping.

Spot transactions will be used by DERs to adjust for deviations between predictions and actual results. Weather variations, changes in markets, and changes in on-site needs will always require adaptation. DER owners can make the adjustments autonomously using price information available on the TE Platform.

## DERs Change the Need for Transmission and Distribution

DERs reduce the need for distribution and transmission facilities and also reduce transport losses because they are close to loads. The benefits of these savings are shared by producers and consumers throughout the system in proportion to their cost and usage.

The feared "death spiral" that utilities face can be avoided by the TE business model because more customers will have long-term transactions for both energy and transport. More customers will stay connected to the grid because grid connection is a benefit to them. They will use the grid to transact when it is in their interest. They will pay their share of the costs of transport through subscriptions and spot transactions like all other parties. They will receive commercial prices for what they sell into the grid.

## Summary

Virtually all the difficulties of the current utilities system to promote and operate DERs are manageable in the TE model. All resources will compete fairly at transparent prices no matter where they are located or how variable their output. This is true regardless of their type, technology, size, location, and ownership.

The risks associated with investments in DERs will be reduced. System efficiency will be enhanced because of fair, transparent competition between technologies.

SECTION 5

# Integrating Microgrids

## Overview

1. TE can be used to coordinate investment and operation inside a microgrid.

2. TE is scalable.

Source: nationalgrid.com

Microgrids are basically a portion of the grid with the capability of operating independently for a period if time. There are many reasons why organizations want to be part of a microgrid, ranging from concept demonstration to military security. The motives are efficiency and reliability.

A university campus may reduce its overall energy costs by integrating all their available resources (PV, combined heat and power, and backup generation) and energy demands (lighting, heating and air conditioning, pumping, and swimming pool heating). By doing this they may be able to reduce their electricity costs below what they would pay the local distribution company.

By operating a microgrid a military base can be assured that it will have reliable electric service even when there is a grid black out or natural disaster. Within the microgrid they can plan to meet their unique needs in an economic way.

## TheTE Model Is Scalable

Forward and spot transactions can be used to coordinate investments within a microgrid and between microgrids.

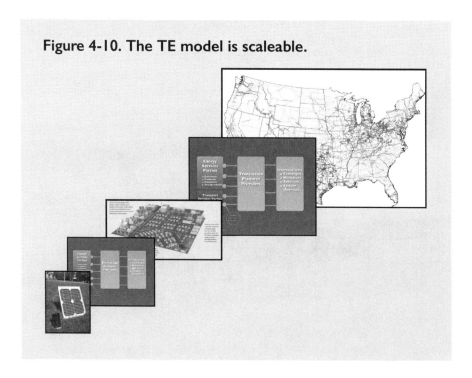

Figure 4-10. The TE model is scaleable.

At the highest level is the national grid. At the next level we have regional or state grids. Then there are towns or municipal grids. Finally, units like small town, industrial parks, military bases, or a university campus can comprise a microgrid. Each of these grids can host one or many TE Platforms (see Figure 4-10).

Even smaller, a home designed to be energy self-sufficient is a microgrid. The home can have a sophisticated energy management system that allocates energy among sources and uses to get the maximum benefit. Individual devices act as energy service groups or parties.

At the extreme, an iPhone connected to a solar panel is a microgrid. Within the iPhone there is very sophisticated algorithm that manages energy use. The goal of the algorithm is to extend life between charges from the solar panel. The battery is an energy service party. The display screen is another.

The TE model works at all levels. In the iPhone the screen trades off energy with computation and communication. In the smart home, a tenders/transactions algorithm can be used to transact energy between air conditioning, water heating, lighting, and storage.

The TE model works as well for a microgrid as it does for the national grid as a whole. The boundaries of the grid are set by the TE Platform.

## Summary

The TE model provides a seamless framework for interactions within microgrids and the grid at large. Forward and spot transactions can be used to coordinate investments and operating decisions at virtually any scale.

SECTION 6

# Integrating the Electric Vehicle

## Overview

1. Automobile manufacturers are putting energy management systems (EMSs) into new vehicles.

2. Vehicle storage is located close to loads.

3. The TE model can integrate vehicle battery storage seamlessly into the utility grid.

4. The TE business model takes advantage of the flexible patterns of electric vehicle charging.

The California Independent System Operator (ISO), California Energy Commission, California Public Utilities Commission, and stakeholders are developing a vehicle for the grid integration roadmap that will support the Governor's 2013 Zero-Emission Vehicles (ZEV) Action Plan. The plan calls for 1.5

million zero-emission vehicles on California roads by 2025. Most of these will be electric vehicles.

California will have a significant new electric demand if these goals are met. If all the electric cars charge at the same time it will add over 10,000 megawatts (state peak demand is now about 60,000 megawatts). The vehicles will not all charge at one time, but this number gives an indication of the potential impact. For comparison, the California state legislature has set targets for new utility storage installation of 1,325 megawatts by 2020.

> *The charge rate on a Nissan Leaf electric car is 80 amps at 220 volts or about 18 kW. The Leaf stores about 24 kWh of energy and the turn-around efficiency is about 85 percent. A Tesla S sedan stores about 85 kWh and charges at 10 to 20 kW. The charge rate is 120 kW at new supercharge sites.*

Electric vehicles (EVs) can be charged whenever and wherever they are not being driven. They can be charged during off-peak hours when drivers are at home, or they can be charged at midday when solar energy is abundant. The TE business model can move vehicle charging to periods when it benefits the vehicle owners and the system. The vehicle batteries provide a convenient place to put excess energy from solar and wind.

Automobile manufacturers are beginning to put energy management systems (EMSs) into vehicles. Many vehicles are equipped with Internet capability. The General Motors OnStar system is a good example. This system is currently available.

Parked vehicles can charge and discharge their onboard batteries in the same way stationary batteries are dispatched. Imagine an EV owner going on vacation for 2 weeks. While gone, the electric vehicle might sit in the garage making a profit on energy exchanges with the grid. (It will keep the cat warm as well.)

## Electric Vehicle Storage Is Close to Demand

EV storage offers the advantage that it is close to rooftop PV panels where power is produced. It is also close to the location where the energy is used. Transport distances are short and therefore the transport energy losses between energy sources, storage, and uses are small.

The average U.S. home uses about 30 kWh (kilowatt-hours) of electricity per day. It is easy to imagine a home with PV panels on the rooftop and an electric vehicle with a 30 kWh battery in the garage. The combination of PV panels and the EV will have an impact on the design and operation of the distribution system of the future. It will reduce investment and operating costs.

The TE business model separates energy and transport services. This separation enables us to integrate the EV into the distribution system in a way that recognizes the vehicle's mobility and storage capability. Electric-vehicle owners will benefit from their contribution to distribution-system savings.

The ability of vehicles to charge and possibly discharge at high rates can put incredible stress on local distribution grid feeders and substations if not managed well. If properly managed, the quickly dispatched energy can be used to reduce the stress on local grids.

There are also reliability benefits associated with the electric vehicle. As mentioned above, the capacity of the vehicle battery is about equivalent to daily electricity use of the average household. The average power outage is a matter of minutes, not days. Stored energy in the vehicle will support homeowners (and their neighbors) through most outages. And an electric vehicle (pure or hybrid) and a solar panel, properly configured could provide basic communication, lighting, and refrigeration services in the event of extended outages.

## Operation of Electric Vehicles Using TE Forward Tenders

We can illustrate the TE operation of electric vehicle charging with an example. An electric-car driver approaches at a charging station at work or home. The driver's iPhone knows the driver's schedule and it informs the vehicle's energy management system (EMS) that the owner needs the car fully charged in a 6-hour window. At its current state of charge the EMS determines 2 hours of charging is required.

The car EMS contacts the TE Platform associated with the charging station and requests buy tenders for the next six hour window. It receives 24, 15-minute buy tenders for energy, and 24 buy tenders for transport for the 6-hour charge window. (Twenty-four is 6 hours times 4, 15-minute periods per hour.) By adding the price of the energy and transport tenders, each 15-minute interval for the 6-hour window gives the total price to charge in each 15-minute interval. The

EMS then searches for the 8, 15-minute intervals with the lowest total prices required to charge the vehicle for a total of 2 hours. The EMS accepts energy and transport transactions for those 8 periods. When the vehicle connects to the charging station it charges at its maximum rate during those periods. The owner has secured the minimum cost charge available in the 6-hour period.

In addition, just for illustration, suppose that after the charging starts the vehicle's EMS receives new buy and sell tenders for the remaining 15-minute intervals in the 6-hour window. The EMS will take the new information and make new buy-and-sell transactions. The EMS continues to do this until the battery is charged. It is possible that the EMS can fill the battery within 6 hours and make a "profit" by charging and discharging the battery at the right times.

A self-optimizing EMS in the vehicle, Cloud computer or the iPhone has plenty of computer power to continuously search to reduce the cost of charging while responding to the physics of the battery, grid conditions, and the preferences of the driver.

## Summary

The TE business model will enable electric-vehicle owners to capture the benefits of both charging flexibility and decentralized storage capacity. This will make electric vehicles more attractive for consumers.

The TE business model integrates the electric vehicle into the grid in a way that utilizes its load-shifting capability, its storage capacity, and its location close to demand.

SECTION 7

# Maintaining Reliability

## Overview

1. Historically "grid custodians," such as federal, state and local agencies have been responsible for maintaining adequate resources to maintain reliability.

2. Increasing deployment of decentralized energy resources (DERs), microgrids, and customer storage, is making centralized planning more difficult.

3. The TE model puts reliability decisions more in the hands of consumers.

4. Grid protection and security will remain in the hands of grid custodians.

The increasing use of variable wind and solar, dispersed storage, decentralized generation, and microgrids, together with the automation of consumer devices, are challenging the traditional definitions of reliability. Data centers, critical communication systems, hospitals, and emergency services typically use backup generation and storage to continue service as a microgrid when grid service is not available.

Severe storms such as hurricanes Katrina and Sandy demonstrate that grid reliability is fragile and extended outages are more frequent than expected. This is one reason why many more customers are turning to decentralized generation and microgrids to improve their own reliability.

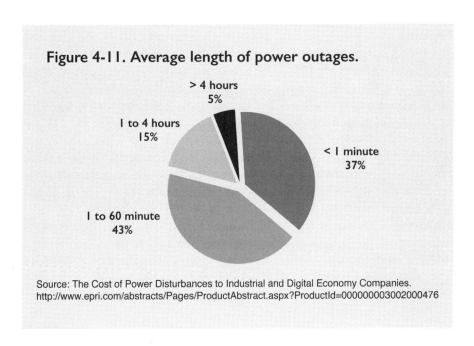

**Figure 4-11. Average length of power outages.**

> 4 hours
5%

1 to 4 hours
15%

< 1 minute
37%

1 to 60 minute
43%

Source: The Cost of Power Disturbances to Industrial and Digital Economy Companies.
http://www.epri.com/abstracts/Pages/ProductAbstract.aspx?ProductId=000000003002000476

Traditionally, the utility and its regulators forecast the future usage of electricity by customers, and they acquired generation, transmission, distribution, and reserves to ensure that customer demands were met with high probability, or reliability, and a reasonable cost.

The TE business model can be accommodated without significant changes to existing reliability standards. The TE model embodies customer self-determination for supply/demand adequacy, and in this way, the customer bears the costs of adequacy and the consequences of inadequacy. The North American Electric Reliability Corporation (NERC) definitions of "reliability" and "adequacy" for the bulk power system have been evolving to the concept of an "Adequate Level of Reliability" (*www.nerc.com/comm/Other/Pages*). This concept permits customers, through self-management and price responsiveness, to determine how much adequacy to purchase.

Most current "grid custodians," such as the Federal Energy Regulatory Commission (FERC), Regional Reliability Coordinators, Public Utility Commissions, and Municipal Boards, establish adequacy standards, including planning reserve margins or loss of load probability. Some regions use forward-capacity markets, and some use procurement by vertically integrated utilities to implement adequacy.

Centralized adequacy planning is becoming more difficult and risky because of increasing deployment of customer-sited solar, combined heat and power (CHP), and fuel cells, It is also complicated by widespread deployment of smart thermostats, smart appliances, and building management systems. It will be difficult for grid custodians to avoid over- or under-procurement. Implementation of TE will support more self-determination of adequacy.

With TE, reliability of transport will be managed by transmission owners and operators with proper investment and maintenance. Access to the transport infrastructure will be sold under forward contracts; spot-tender prices will be set to prevent unreliable overuse of the grid while at the same time providing for emergency actions to curtail electricity generation and usage.

Widespread deployment of TE will ensure that customers purchase an adequate level of energy. Their investments will be guided by forward tenders, whereas spot tenders will ensure that customers respond rationally to current grid conditions.

## Summary

In summary, adequacy is largely a matter of customer choice within the TE business model. Forward and spot transactions are allowed to reflect market surpluses and shortages. Customers with self-generation, microgrids, smart devices, and smart buildings have more direct control over the adequacy and reliability choices.

Overall, reliability, grid protection, and security will remain under the control of grid custodians, such as reliability coordinators. However, the TE roadmap (see Chapter 6) envisions a continuing and evolving role for today's grid custodians, including FERC, NERC, Regional Reliability Coordinators, Balancing Authorities, Public Utility Commissions, and Municipal Boards. Microgrids will have their own grid custodians.

CHAPTER 5

# Why Transactive Energy?

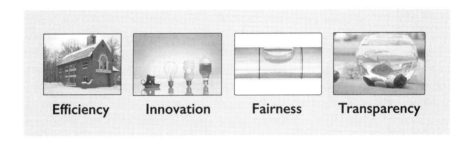

Efficiency    Innovation    Fairness    Transparency

In this chapter we discuss the advantages of the Transactive Energy (TE) business model and we explain why we think the electricity markets should move toward TE. The first reason is efficiency. Our energy use must be more efficient if we are going to reduce greenhouse gas emissions. The second reason is innovation. Moore's Law and the Internet have created the potential for unprecedented market innovations that will be enabled by the TE model. In addition, the TE model is fair and transparent.

# Improving Efficiency

## Overview

1. The potential for reducing electricity use (without compromising service) is significant.

2. The efficiency gains will come from both smart investment and smart operation.

3. Forward transactions enable consumers and producers to reduce the risk associated with efficiency investments.

4. Transactions based on location will support investments in decentralized resources.

5. TE promotes coordinated operation of thermal, wind, solar, and storage.

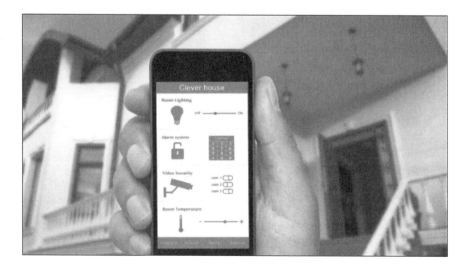

We need to reduce our dependence on fossil fuels in economically efficient ways. We can do this by converting to renewable energy sources and by reducing waste. Both of these are enabled by the TE business model.

In the United States there are tremendous opportunities for saving money by reducing energy consumption. It is particularly important to reduce electricity consumption because for every kilowatt-hour (kWh) of electricity consumed from the grid we consume about three kWh of energy. (The thermal efficiency of fossil-fuel power plants is from 30% to 50%.) Transmission and distribution system transport results in additional loss of about 7% and much more when the grid is highly loaded.

The Rocky Mountain Institute (*www.rmi.org/reinventingfire*) believes we can economically reduce the building sector's use of primary energy from 40% to 70% by 2050. It will take the right economic signals to make this happen.

The story of the Nest Learning Thermostat provides a good example of how the savings will be accomplished. An article in a recent issue of the MIT Technology Review gives us a glimpse into what Silicon Valley is bringing to the sort of mundane world of home heating and cooling. The article is part of a feature titled, "50 Disruptive Companies" (See *www2.technologyreview.com/tr50/2013/* .) According to the article, Tony Fadell, the Apple Computer executive who created the iPod and played a key role in developing the iPhone, was building a new home in near Lake Tahoe in California. He asked the question, "How do I design this home when the primary interface to my world is the thing in my pocket (the iPhone)?" When it came to choosing a programmable thermostat for his eco-friendly heating, ventilation, and air conditioning (HVAC) system he blew a gasket. "The thermostats were 500 bucks a pop, and they were horrible and doing nothing and brain-dead." He decided to design his own thermostat.

The result is the new Nest thermostat. The thermostat sells for about $200. It is attractive: Virtually all the controls are on the user-friendly iPhone.

Compared to the "smart meter" the Nest thermostat is genius. After the homeowner has adjusted it 10 or 15 times it begins to understand what it is supposed to do. It begins to anticipate when the building should be warmed and when it should be cooled.

The Nest thermostats detect human activity in the home. They adjust demand a few minutes after activity stops in the morning. They infer that people have gone to work or school. It's easy to see the day when the thermostat will use global positioning system (GPS) signals from the iPhone to anticipate when occupants are headed home. The thermostats will welcome them with a home at the perfect temperature.

It isn't hard to foresee the future: The Nest thermostat will evolve into the Nest energy management system (EMS), or perhaps a network of communicating EMSs for several devices. It will communicate among the important applianc-es via wireless connection (Wi-Fi.) It will sense the occupancy and activities of people in the home. When owners are away, it will know where they are and how they are moving, and will interact with outside information suppliers like the weather service.

The EMS of the future will predict our energy needs hours, days, months, and years in advance. It will manage energy use and energy purchases in a way that optimizes cost and benefit.

# Efficiency Gains Result from Both Investment and Operation

Investments in efficiency are often viewed as risky. They entail new designs, new technology, and new materials. The savings are uncertain and are realized over a long time frame.

For example, lighting savings come from a combination of investment and operation. We buy an efficient light bulb. It is an investment. The savings will depend on how smart we are about operating the bulb. We can put a motion sensor in the room so the light is on only when the room is occupied, or we can push the switch up and down by hand. The motion sensor will reduce operating costs. Will it reduce cost enough to pay for the sensor? TE will give customers the means to answer that question using forward tenders and transactions.

# Forward Transactions Will Allow Building Owners to Lock in Savings and Reduce Risk

General Electric has introduced a new hybrid electric water heater, the GeoSpring. (*See www.geappliances.com/heat-pump-hot-water-heater* .) The heater does most of its heating with a heat pump. The heat pump is backed up with a small resistive heating element.

The 50-gallon hybrid water heater costs about $1,100. It saves an estimated $365 every year in water heating expenses. The savings are based on Department of Energy (DOE) test procedures. The GeoSpring is compared to 50-gallon standard electric tank water heaters. Standard heaters use 4,879 kWh per year versus 1,830 kWh for the GeoSpring. The calculations are based on a national average electricity rate of 12 cents per kWh.

The investment for a standard 50-gallon water-heating unit is $325. Thus, the GeoSpring unit will potentially pay for the extra $775 investment in about 2 or 3 years. That assumes your operation is the same as the operation assumed for the savings calculation. What if your needs are different from the standard, which is highly likely?

In the TE business model you will be able to use an iPhone application (app) and your EMS to forecast your hot water needs based on your past usage and other available information (see Figure 5-1). The app will go to a TE Platform and use the forward tender price information there to estimate your savings.

This will greatly reduce the risk of your efficiency investment. Based on this estimate, you can sell the energy savings from your forward energy subscription on a TE Platform in a long-term transaction that should more than offset your investment.

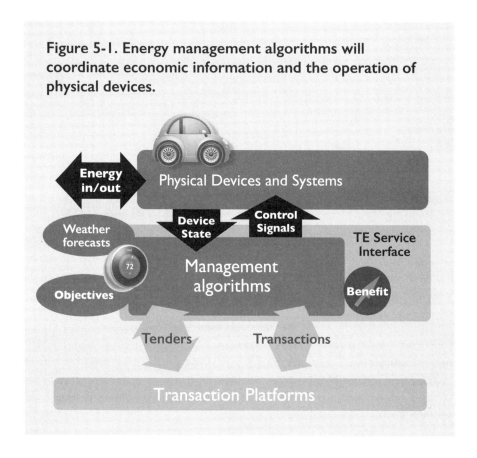

**Figure 5-1. Energy management algorithms will coordinate economic information and the operation of physical devices.**

## Spot Transactions Permit Customers to Deal with Surprises

Once the GeoSpring is operating, the EMS and a TE Platform will provide additional savings. The EMS will use spot transactions to adjust water-heater usage and compensate for any variations from the forecast. Most importantly, because the water heater is a thermal storage device, the EMS can heat water when the forward tenders prices are low or negative and avoid heating water when prices are high. The EMS can make these transactions while ensuring that there is always enough hot water to meet the owner's needs. This will reduce the risk of not getting a payback on the investment. It will move use toward low-cost wind and solar. It will avoid the use of fossil fuels.

## Summary

The TE business model uses forward and spot transactions to coordinate investment and operating decisions throughout the ecosystem. Efficiency is coordinated at the level of devices, buildings, neighborhoods, and regions.

Risk management and operating savings will occur throughout the electricity ecosystem. The result will be big gains in building efficiency and ultimately lower investment on both the producer and consumer sides of the meter. According to Amory Lovins in his book Reinventing Fire:

> For most people, electricity service is a bit like buying an early Model T: you can have any color you want as long as it's black.
>
> But this passive consumption of electricity is on the brink of a radical shift. Advances in information technology (IT) and the smart grid technologies that combine IT with the electric grid are enabling bidirectional control, distributed intelligence, two-way communication, ubiquitous real-time price information, and demand response. These new technologies are creating the opportunity to capture new value for customers and providers, old and new. For example, automated controls can imperceptibly respond to price signals by adjusting appliances' usage, allowing customers to minimize their costs with no hassle and with an uncompromised experience, just as ATMs and the Internet have done in banking.[1]

The TE business model is a realization of the future Amory Lovins has described. It will be a key to the 40%–70% reduction in building electricity use as predicted by the Rocky Mountain Institute.

---

[1] Amory Lovins, Reinventing Fire: Bold Business Solutions for the New Energy Era (Chelsea Green Publishing, 2011), p.196

# More Innovation

## Overview

1. The TE business model will increase innovation by:

* reducing investment risk for all players, retail, and wholesale.
* providing transparent, predictable, and actionable prices to everyone.
* stimulating new services and technology.

2. We need innovation throughout the electricity ecosystem to:

* improve efficiency.
* reduce reliance on fossil fuels.
* lower costs.

Moore's Law and the Internet will revolutionize electric power markets. The whole smart-grid paradigm is the result of innovation made possible by improvements in computation, connection, and communication. The TE business model opens up new opportunities for innovation.

Innovation is bound to blossom when customers and producers can coordinate their investment and operating decisions using forward and spot transactions.

The McKinsey Global Institute has just published a survey of the benefits of disruptive technologies to the year 2025. Mobile internet, automation of knowledge work, the internet of things, and Cloud technology are at the top of their list. See "Disruptive technologies: Advances that will transform life, business, and the global economy." (*www.mckinsey.com/insights/business_technology/disruptive_technologies*) The TE model applies these technologies to electricity. Energy storage and renewable energy are on the McKinsey list of top 12 disruptors as well. The success of storage and renewables depends on the items at the top of the list.

Today, where flat, $/kWh prices are paid by customers there is reduced incentive for customers to buy smart appliances and invest in energy management systems (EMSs). As a result there is little incentive for manufacturers to invent and offer appliances and devices with two-way communication. These devices are a little more expensive. Manufacturers are waiting for markets to develop so they can use economies of scale to drive down costs.

The Transactive Energy (TE) model puts the incentives in place for the innovation and disruptive technologies to facilitate energy efficiency, storage, DERs, and renewables. The size of the impacts on innovation will depend on how widespread TE is implemented.

In the TE model, retail customers can do all the things that big producers can do. Customers can execute forward transactions for the energy they sell into the grid. Transactions are easy and automatic. Consumers and producers connect to the same TE Platforms and speak the same language.

The use of forward transactions by everyone in the market will allow new ways of reducing risk. It is a routine practice for large producers to use forward transactions to reduce investment risk. For example, when XYZ Incorporated wants to build a new solar facility in the California desert they first negotiate a contract with Pacific Gas and Electric, Southern California Edison, and/or San Diego Gas and Electric to purchase the energy produced at a specified price (for the next 20 years.)

XYZ's forward transactions significantly reduce the risk of their investment. As a result, they are able to recruit investors, borrow money at lower interest rates, and increase their profits. If there is a tax loophole, or a way to reduce risk management, the sophisticated parties in the production side of electric power-er can find them. In the TE model retail customers will have the same smart-access as big producers.

Large wholesale producers can also operate their facilities profitably because they know the prices of spot tenders for each of the next several 15-minute intervals. They know when it is profitable to run a combustion turbine or charge a storage device. When TE is implemented customers will have the same infor-mation. Their smart thermostat or smart appliance will know how to operate profitably— across the entire electricity ecosystem.

We are in an era of innovation in services as well as technology. The TE business model will encourage creation of transaction platforms, intermediaries, market makers, and EMS systems. New people with new skills and expertise will bring innovation to electricity.

Certainly there is a long list of services that can be provided in innovative ways if market signals are available. As Amory Lovins says in his book ReInventing Fire, ".. automated controls can imperceptibly respond to price signals by adjusting appliances usage, allowing customers to minimize their costs with no hassle and with an uncompromised experience, just as ATM's and the Internet have done in banking." In other words, The TE business model and technology will do for electric power what ATM's and the internet have done in banking.

## Summary

Stability, fairness, and transparency support innovation. They are keys to encouraging small entrepreneurs. The TE model offers more stability, fairness, and transparency than our current top-down, centralized, complex, command and control system.

In the TE model, short- and long-term rules are clear and transparent. This will encourage rapid decision-making by entrepreneurs and reward them for doing the right things. Lower risk will inspire entrepreneurs to pursue more opportunities.

TE will increase innovation by reducing investment risk and providing better cost information to decision-makers. Forward transactions will reduce invest-ment risk for producers and consumers alike. Spot transactions will provide entrepreneurs the incentives they need to develop smart devices of all kinds:

appliances, storage devices, building energy management systems, and industrial process controllers. TE will encourage rapid decision-making and will reward the right things.

Innovation is the key to improving efficiency, lowering cost, and decreasing our reliance on fossil fuels. It is difficult to imagine a business model that is more friendly to innovation than Transactive Energy. The model enables small and large customers to transact on a level playing field with small and large producers.

SECTION 3

# More Fair

## Overview

1. TE provides a level playing field: Small parties have the same access to the market as large parties.

2. Energy and transport services are separated. Customers pay for what they need and use.

3. The TE model meets the goals of California ratemaking. (Other jurisdictions are similar.)

4. California has bifurcated the goals of fair rate design and secure electric service for the poor and disabled.

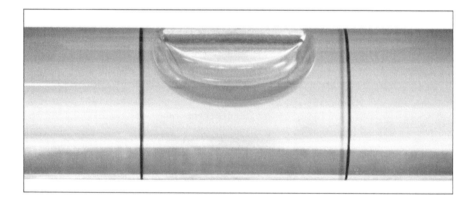

The TE business model provides a level playing field for all technologies. All ways to make or save energy can compete fairly regardless of their type, technology, size, location, and ownership. This possibility has been the dream of rate-makers and stakeholders.

Consumers can buy energy directly from sources they choose, or consumers can buy whatever type of energy they prefer if it is available: "green" or otherwise. It is as easy as telling StubHub, the event transaction platform, where you would like to sit in the baseball park.

All technologies compete fairly. The tenders and transactions agreed to by a supplier take into account the operating characteristics of the technology whether it is a combustion turbine or a smart appliance.

The TE product is a unit of energy delivered during a time period at a given place. It does not matter how the energy was produced or saved, unless of course the transaction is for a specific type of production such as renewables.

Location differences are accounted for in transport transactions. Decentralized resources pay less for transportation if they are located close to their customers. Customers pay less for transport if they are close to their suppliers.

In the TE model, energy produced by publicly owned utilities is treated exactly the same as energy produced by privately held producers or prosumers. Ownership of production and transport are separated so that producers and transporters compete fairly. Generation costs cannot be hidden in the cost of distribution and vice versa.

## California Ensures Equitable Rates

In California, the goal of electricity rate-making (pricing) is to ensure rates that are both equitable and affordable while meeting policy objectives.

California rate-making follows the following five general principles:

> 1) Rates should be based on marginal costs.
> 2) Rates should be based on cost-causation principles.
> 3) Rates should encourage conservation and reduce peak demand.
> 4) Rates should provide stability, simplicity, and customer choice.
> 5) Rates should encourage economically efficient decision-making.

The TE model is completely consistent with these principles. Spot transactions in the TE model reflect the marginal costs of production, storage, and transport. Spot transaction prices also rise above production costs when there is scarcity or transport congestion.

Investment and operating costs are recovered in forward and spot transactions. The TE model encourages conservation and peak demand reduction by moving demand away from expensive periods and toward inexpensive periods.

Forward transactions introduce stability into the system. The TE model is simple and it affords the ultimate in consumer choice. Retail customers play on the same level playing field with large industrial customers.

The TE model reduces risk (and therefore cost) for investment decisions. TE encourages rational trade-offs between production and conservation no matter how complicated the situation is.

## Low-Income Subsidies

In some places, such as California, the legislature or another body will mandate lower prices for low-income customers. Without debating the merits of this idea, lowering the $/kWh prices will decrease the customers incentive to be more efficient and to use energy when it is least expensive.

Subsidies can be implemented within the TE model. One way is to provide some customers with a subscription for their typical usage at a discounted monthly cost. If the low-income customer needs less, the customer's EMS system will automatically sell the extra energy at current tender prices and pay the customer. If the customer uses more, the customer will pay the current tender price. And if the customer buys a more efficient air conditioner, his investment cost can be offset by selling part of his long-term subscription at forward prices. In this way, fairness and conservation can be accomplished.

## Summary

In summary, the TE model meets all of the goals of California rate-making. The TE model uses forward and spot tenders and transactions to coordinate investment and operating decisions throughout the electricity ecosystem. While the implementation requires sophisticated communication and information technology (CIT), the concepts are clear and simple.

## SECTION 4

# More Transparent

## Overview

1. TE rules are simple and straightforward.

2. Current tariff designs are complex.

3. Tariffs are difficult for consumers and producers to understand.

4. They will not get simpler if we follow current business models.

Electricity pricing is complex and confusing the way it is done today. Investor-owned utilities (IOUs) typically have many ways of charging customers. Pacific Gas and Electric in California has over seventy electric service tariffs in their tariff book.

A "full-requirements tariff" with increasing block prices for monthly energy, combined with time-of-use (TOU) and fixed-monthly charges, is very difficult for a customer to understand. A time of use tariff, combined with a demand charge and a fixed charge, is difficult for a customer to work with. In some situations, usage in a 15-minute interval may increase a customer's bill for the entire month or year. Dynamic pricing information, event-based demand response, and net metering are often layered on top of other tariffs.

The TE business model eliminates the need for these complex tariffs. They are replaced by a single enabling tariff agreement that applies to all transactions between any two parties, such as the utility and its customer or between the two parties. Energy and transport are treated as two separate products.

The simple enabling TE tariff agreement does not specify prices or amount of energy to be bought or sold. It is simply a commercial agreement that says for each transaction they may execute under the agreement the seller will deliver the transacted product at the agreed location and time period. The buyer agrees to take delivery and to pay the seller the agreed cost of the transaction. The enabling agreement/tariff has payment and credit and default provisions.

With TE everyone plays by the same clear rules. If you want energy then you accept the tender of a seller or you make a tender for your needs that may be accepted by a seller. If you are producing energy then you offer tenders to sell. You set the price and quantity or you accept a tender of a buyer. If things do not work out the way you expected, then you make adjustments according to the same simple rules. There are intermediaries affiliated with the TE Platforms to help you.

Most of the minute-to-minute decisions will be made by automated agents acting on your behalf. The agents will be embedded in your home, your appliances, you car, and your office building. No need to wade through tariff books and say yes to something you don't understand. You tell your energy management system (EMS) what you want and go about your life confident that your agent is doing smart things on your behalf. It is "set and forget."

It's somewhat like buying baseball tickets using StubHub. You tell StubHub what you want and what you are willing to pay and it uses a sophisticated algorithm to sort through all the options to come up with the best deals for you. It happens at the speed of light.

## Data on Tenders and Transactions

The TE Platform database will hold information on all transactions in the system. Regulators will be able to use this data to ensure that rules are being followed and there are no economic abuses. With strict protection of private information, economists can access the data to study the efficiency and stability of the system. The database will be a tremendous resource for researchers.

Everyone will use a common protocol so anybody can transact with anybody else at prices and in amounts both parties know ahead of time and agree to (see Chapter 3).

## Summary

Transparency is fundamental to how decisions are made. It is a key ingredient of trust. Customers and producers may not want to get involved directly, but they do want to be confident that decisions are open and that rules and process are being followed.

The TE model offers the possibility of a highly transparent system at three levels. The first level of transparency is its simplicity. The TE model is simpler and far more adaptable than our current tariff systems. The second level of transparency is the availability of data on all transactions by producer and consumer. A third level of transparency will be the use of a common protocol for payments among the parties.

CHAPTER 6

# How Do We Get There From Here?

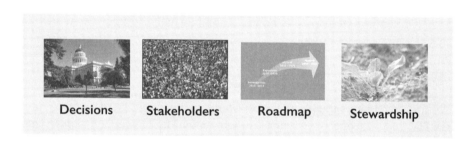

Decisions    Stakeholders    Roadmap    Stewardship

This chapter outlines the actions we believe are necessary to make a smooth transition to the Transactive Energy (TE) business and regulatory model. We use California as a case study. The California economy is the twelfth largest economy in the world. The State of California is at the forefront of the move toward a sustainable electric power system. The State can provide a model for the rest of the world to follow.

Several important steps are needed to accomplish the transition from the legislatively enforced fixed-price model we have today to the TE business and regulatory model:

1) Frame the policy decisions properly and involve the right people.
2) Establish a semi-autonomous Stewardship Board to monitor and enable the transition.
3) Use pilots (prototypes) to develop new processes and systems.
4) Take actions to mitigate impacts on stakeholders, particularly customers and investor-owned utilities (IOUs.)

We envision a process that begins with pilot projects in areas where the TE model offers a solution to a problem (see Figure 6-1). A potential problem is integrating decentralized storage resources and electric vehicles into the grid or managing the load to compensate for the variability of renewables, load, and

conventional generation. The pilots might also be a response to overly complicated tariff structures and a desire to make things simpler and more transparent.

The pilots will bubble up from the energy ecosystem and should not wait for
legislation. The California Public Utilities Commission (CPUC), California Energy Commission (CEC), U.S. Department of Energy, and others can help finance
and create these TE pilots. The pilots will provide the hard data needed to guide
policy changes.

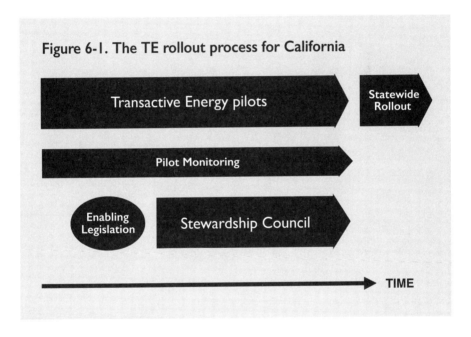

**Figure 6-1. The TE rollout process for California**

The first large pilots will probably be developed by IOUs, municipalities, college
campuses, or military bases. The City of San Francisco and Marin County want
to contract for their energy outside of Pacific Gas and Electric (PG&E). Customers in these cities could use the TE model to contract for energy supplies with
customers and suppliers.

Several microgrids are emerging in California. Some of these might use the TE
model to coordinate the design, building, and operation of their systems.

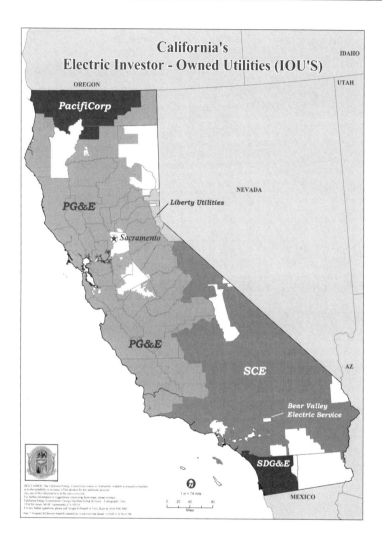

Most of California is currently served by monopoly IOUs that provide both energy and transport to most residential customers and many commercial customers. Some large commercial and industrial customers already can buy directly from other parties while still paying the IOUs for distribution services.

Enabling State legislation will be desirable to address the following:

1) Form a semi-autonomous "Transactive Energy Stewardship Board." Semi-autonomous boards have been used successfully in California for

other policy implementations. A Blue Ribbon Task Force was first used during the creation of a network of marine reserves the length of the state. A Citizen's Redistricting Commission was also used to oversee voter redistricting.

2) Direct the Stewardship Board to oversee the evolution of the State toward a single tariff model. The model will be used by all parties for retail transactions of both energy and transport. Decisions by the Board will be based on sound science and the interests of all stakeholders.

The Stewardship Board should be charged to study and make recommendations on the timing of direct access to energy and transport transactions for all customers. The Board should propose phase-in schedules for standard TE Platforms and protocols for use statewide.

If the legislature takes the necessary actions, then the system will be set to transition without further intervention. Parties doing what is in their interest will drive the electricity ecosystem toward efficiency in a fair and transparent way.

Regulatory oversight will be required of the distribution transport owners by the CPUC, the transmission transport and wholesale generation by the Federal Energy Regulatory Commission (FERC), and North American Electric Reliability Corporation (NERC.) Retail TE transactions will be overseen by the CPUC, and the wholesale TE transactions by FERC.

## The Rest of This Chapter

In the remaining Sections we cover in more detail the following topics:

1) Legislative decisions that are needed to implement the TE model.
2) Impacts on key stakeholders. (Most impacts are positive. Actions can be taken to mitigate potential negative impacts.)
3) Roadmap. The detailed steps that need to be taken.
4) Stewardship Board.

Can we convert the California market to an efficient, fair, and transparent system? There is every reason to believe we can, and if we can move to the TE model, then we are well on our way to realizing the dream of an efficient, environmentally friendly electric power system. Importantly, if California can accomplish this transition then it will provide a model for the rest of the world.

# Legislative Decisions

## Overview

1. Several decisions need to be made by the State legislature in order for California to transition smoothly to the TE business and regulatory model.

2. The decisions include the following:

- What is the time-frame for completing the transition to the TE model?
- Do we create a Stewardship Board to supervise the transition?
- What is the scope of the Stewardship Board's work?
- What is the budget and where does the money come from?

Decisions help to focus the public dialog on critical actions. Decisions also guide research and information-gathering efforts. This section is about the decisions that we believe need to be made by the California legislature in order to implement the Transactive Energy (TE) model in California.

We are proposing a set of State actions that will enable the transition of California's current business and regulatory model for IOUs to the TE model.

The current system uses a maze of tariffs to legislatively enforce prices. Currently, each of the IOUs have about seventy tariffs. The tariffs are very complex and often direct load control (DLC), event-based demand response (DR) and Net Metering programs are layered on top of the current tariffs. This adds to the complexity.

The new model will use forward and spot transactions to coordinate investment and operating decisions throughout the electric energy ecosystem. It will be easier for customers to understand and will save money.

Changing the business and regulatory model is a big goal. It won't happen overnight. However, we think with the proper legislative changes it can happen fairly rapidly without significant disruption. The wholesale part of the California market is already close to the TE model. The legislative actions outlined here would move the TE concept into the retail markets.

We are not yet proposing a TE transition process for public utilities, such as municipals; that is a subject for further discussion and leadership by the public utilities themselves. Public utilities that are not investor-owned serve about 3 million customers in California. Such utilities often participate in wholesale forward and spot markets. We believe that the public utilities will discover great benefits for their customers and their utility from the implementation of TE.

## The Transition Strategy

The strategy we recommend includes four decisions that involve setting deadlines for the conversion of customers to the TE tariff, creation of the Stewardship Board, the scope of the Board's responsibility, and the size of Board's budgets (see Figure 6-2). The white ovals in the figure describe the "status quo" strategy. The green boxes describe the "TE strategy."

## Figure 6-2. Legislative decisions.

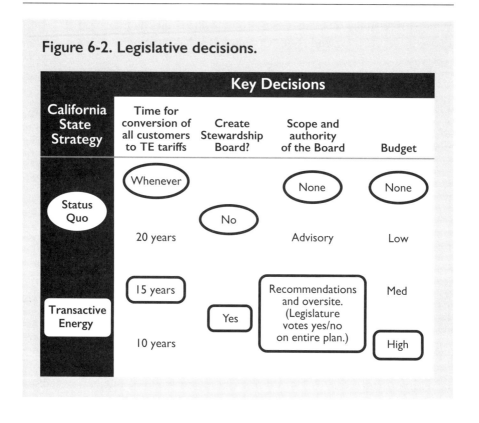

## Timing

When the Marine Life Protection Act (MLPA) was passed in 1999, the California State legislature directed the Department of Fish and Game to design and implement a network of marine reserves along the coast of California. They gave the Department 11 years to make it happen. In 2009 the State took a similar approach with the redesign of the voting districts.

We think the State should take the same approach with Transactive Energy. The legislature should set clear objectives, specify responsibility, and establish a deadline when the transformation should be complete. A deadline for completion would establish the pace of change, milestones, and required budgets.

Progress of the rollout can be measured in terms of the number (or percentage) of retail customers on the standard TE tariff. It is a straightforward, easily observable number.

We believe the objective should be to have the TE model fully implemented statewide in 10 to 20 years. Even with the standard TE tariff there will be support for fixed-price tariffs and low-income discounts. The sooner the transformation takes place, the sooner the benefits will be realized.

## Stewardship Board

Implementation of the MLPA was accomplished by appointing a Blue Ribbon Task Force to make network design recommendations to the State. The Board oversaw a public process that involved many experts and multitudes of stakeholders.

Recently, the Little Hoover Commission on California State Government Organization and Economy recommended that "the Governor and the Legislature should develop a plan to modernize energy governance. (*See www.lhc.ca.gov/about/about.html* .) Organizational reform ultimately is essential if the state is to realize its manifold energy and environmental goals and reduce the risk of another profoundly expensive policy failure."

The Little Hoover Commission further recommended that serious consideration be given to "establishment of a Secretary of Energy, reporting to the Governor, and the consolidation of all energy policy under one agency or commission with the Secretary of Energy serving as agency secretary or commission chair." The recommended deadline for the reorganization was December 2014.

A TE Stewardship Board would fit well into the recommended structure. The Secretary of Energy could be the chair of the Board. The mission of the Board and the process of selecting members would be specified by the legislature.

Transparency and stakeholder participation are key elements of a successful policy process. The MLPA and voter redistricting are good models for how this can be accomplished.

## Scope and Authority of the Electricity Stewardship Board

Energy policy is hotly debated in California. The debate goes on in proceedings and lobbying at the CPUC, the California Independent System Operator (CAISO), CEC, the governor's office and the legislature. Many consumer, environmental, industry, and utility groups participate in this advocacy process. There are so many overlapping processes that many participants are overwhelmed by the complexity and costs of participation. Moreover, when governor, legislature, and lobbies become involved, the outcome of the processes are not transparent. The decisions and outcomes are not always positive, even for those with political power. This was evidenced by the decisions and outcomes of California Assembly Bill AB 1890.

## There are two basic alternatives for defining the scope and authority of the Stewardship Board.

The first alternative is for the Board to be granted full authority to develop a plan with advice of its technical experts and the input of all parties; to direct its implementation; to monitor the results; and to make adjustments for transition of the IOUs and retail customers in the IOU service areas to the TE model. The legislature could only reject or accept the entire plan of the Board with an up or down vote and at the same time approve the recommended changes to the Public Utilities Code.

Alternatively, the Board plans could be advisory and the legislature could then decide on its implementation.

We recommend the first alternative because the politics of energy policy have proven to be extremely challenging and have led to failure as in the case of AB 1890.

## Budget

The Stewardship Board will need a budget in order to make and implement decisions. The Board will have a staff of consultants, contractors, and expenses. The Board will monitor projects, facilitate public participation, and support communication activities, and reporting. They may fund pilots and prototype development or recommend the funding by the IOUs and the CPUC.

The direct cost of the Marine Life Protection Act (MLPA) Initiative was about $25 million. It was funded from public and private sources. The voter redistricting project cost about $7 million. (It was grossly underfunded according to people involved.) Both of these efforts were funded from a combination of public and private sources. The exact budget for TE depends on the mission and timing of the business and regulatory model conversion.

The cost of these efforts should be compared with the cost of the current regulatory process and the cost of missed opportunities if changes are delayed. It is important to note that both the MLPA Initiative and the California statewide voter redistricting are regarded as major policy implementation successes. They were both completed on time.

## Summary

For the best possible results, the decision to implement the TE business and regulatory model statewide will have to be made by the California legislature. The pace of the change should be set by the legislation, just as it was with the MLPA and voter redistricting. The legislature also needs to specify mission, makeup, and budget for a Stewardship Board.

The focus of change should be on changing retail tariff structures from legislatively enforced tariffs based on fixed prices to a system of forward subscriptions and spot transactions. The legislation should also be clear that the intent is to separate energy and transport services.

The ultimate goals are lower energy service costs through greater efficiency and lower investment risk by small investors. Less energy use together with the shift to renewables will result in less carbon emissions.

The current energy system is overly complicated and it does not provide customers and decentralized energy developers with the information they need to make investment and operating decisions that are consistent with social goals.

The IOUs are concerned with the future viability of their business model. The model is threatened by increasing self-generation by customers and the resulting decrease in revenues from those customers. Customers want reasonable costs of electric service and the right to make their own choices for electricity self-supply or purchased supply. Customers with self-supply want the option to sell their excess supply at fair prices.

The State is passing policies to increase distributed generation, storage, and solar and wind electricity technologies. Successful implementation of these policies requires coordination of operation and investment and contractual obligations among the parties. The TE model offers the promise of resetting the system for everyone's benefit—and sparking statewide innovation.

# Stakeholder Impacts

## Overview

1. Customers will have more choices and less risk.

2. IOU's will be challenged to make changes, capture the opportunities, and protect their shareholders interests.

3. At first, the changes may not be optimal for some parties. The Steward-ship Board will be charged with mitigating negative impacts.

Ultimately, customers and the general public will be better off with a TE system. The improvements in investment and operating decisions will result in higher efficiency. The use of forward transactions will lower risk for all customers and producers.

The Rocky Mountain Institute estimates that improvement in U.S. building efficiency alone can save $1.9 trillion net present value over the next 35 years. The cost of reaching this goal is estimated to be $.5 trillion. (California would account for about 10% of these savings based on population.) We will only get a fraction of this with the complicated command and control systems we have today.

Can we make the transition to the TE model while mitigating any negative impacts? We are going to eventually change tariff structures for all customers and there will be positive and negative impacts in the short term, but the structure of TE subscriptions can help mitigate impacts. The potential benefits of TE are many.

## IOU Impacts

When TE is in place customers and producers will see more options; they will be able to make smarter investment and consumption decisions, and their investments will be less risky. IOUs across the United States are beginning to see some serious threats to their current business and regulatory model. One threat is the so-called, "death spiral" caused by DERs, prosumers, and microgrids (see Chapter 2, Section 4).

A switch to the TE model offers an opportunity to mitigate or stop the spiral and reset the system. IOUs can enter into forward transactions (subscriptions) with customers to cover their fixed cost of distribution. Every customer, such as a homeowner, would subscribe to a share of the distribution system that they would pay for using monthly payments. If they sold their home then the subscription would be passed to the new homeowner or paid off. If a homeowner decided to self-generate then they could sell a portion of the subscription on a TE Platform. If they used the distribution grid during peak usage or during emergencies, and used more than they subscribed to in that time period, they might pay a high price.

In the long run, TE will create opportunities for IOUs to innovate with fewer regulatory constraints. IOUs can take the lead in creating Transactive Energy Platforms and developing the new infrastructure.

## Customer Impacts

We have discussed the benefits to customers and DERs in several chapters of this book. Generally, TE will save customers money over time, reduce the volatility of their bills, and give them more opportunities to self-generate, sell energy to others, and buy from whomever they choose.

Any time tariff changes are considered some will pay less and others will pay more. Advocates for low-income customers will be especially concerned. Equity among customer groups can be addressed within the TE model with explicit side payments that reduce the initial fixed monthly subscription payments for some, while increasing payments for others. These are political and fairness decisions best made by the Stewardship Board.

## Changes for Current Players and Roles for New Players

Implementation of the TE Platform will bring some changes for current players (see Table 6-1).

| Table 6-1. Impacts of Transactive Energy Model on Current Players | | |
|---|---|---|
| **CURRENT PLAYER** | | **CHANGE** |
| Energy Service Parties | Retail customers | Simple tariff; self-dispatch of generation, storage, and usage; smarter investment and consumption decisions, less investment risk. |
| | Wholesale customers | Same as above. |
| | Decentralized Energy Resources (DERs) | Same as above. Self-dispatch and less investment risk. |
| Transport Service Parties | Transmission Owner Operators | No significant change. |
| | Distribution Owner/ Operators | Enter into long-term commercial subscriptions and reduce risk, more opportunity to innovate in services. |
| Independent System Operators (ISOs) | | Little change. Simplification of ISO tariffs and processes. Rely more on the price responsiveness of customers and DER. Very high ISO price caps and very low ISO price floors. |
| Regulators | | Focus more on market rules and less on planning and tariff administration. |

There will also be some new players in the electricity ecosystem (see Table 6-2). One new set of players will be the operators of TE Platforms. There will be several platforms, all adhering to the same standard design and implementing the same standard TE protocols. Initially, Some of the platforms may be owned by IOUs and other energy and transport service parties.

| Table 6-2. New roles and responsibilities | |
|---|---|
| **NEW ROLES** | **RESPONSIBILITY** |
| TE Platform Operator(s) | Recording tenders and transactions. Communication and information management (CIT), database management. Calculation of payments among the parties for transactions. |
| Exchanges | Enable continuous forward and spot markets. Support forward and spot system balance. |
| Market Makers | Market liquidity facilitation (no speculation allowed). |
| Competitive Retail Energy Providers | Sell and buy energy to retail customers using standard TE tariffs and platforms. |
| Energy Managment System and Device Control Vendors | Sell and support energy managment systems for customer facilities and DER that adhere to TE standard protocols and control various customer devices for the benefit of customers. |

As the Stewardship Board recommends, new competitive retail providers will develop. They will be required to use the standard TE tariff and standard TE Platforms.

When the need arises exchanges will form. These will be licensed and overseen by the CPUC or FERC. These exchanges will enable the forward and spot markets and facilitate the balance of supply and demand.

Market makers can facilitate transactions by continuously posting buy-and-sell tenders for a range of forward intervals.

The market makers will be regulated and prohibited from accumulating significant buy-or-sell positions. They will be allowed a maximum buy/sell price spread.

Market makers will not be permitted to speculate or be owned by any of the market participants. Market makers for regulated transport products owned by regulated transport operators may be the exception. They will typically make money from their buy/sell spread. This market making function will be highly automated.

We can expect a flurry of activity as IOUs and vendors develop and deploy energy management and control systems for customer devices, appliances, facilities, and DERs that adhere to the standard TE protocols.

## Summary

The Stewardship Board will have many tools to mitigate the short and long-term impacts on various stakeholder categories while unleashing cost savings and innovation that will benefit nearly all stakeholder categories.

**SECTION 3**

# Roadmap

## Overview

1. Planners are thinking about transitioning to the Transactive Energy model.

2. A comprehensive roadmap for TE rollout has been published.

3. The migration the TE model does not require "big bang" implementation.

4. Pilot projects can lead the way.

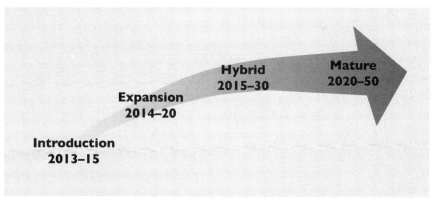

*Stages in a US national Transactive Energy roadmap that was developed in 2012 by Edward Cazalet and a team of Transactive Energy leaders.*

It is useful to have a conceptual roadmap so we can visualize where we are and where we are going. Since 2009, one of our authors, Edward Cazalet, has worked with the Smart Grid Interoperability Panel (SGIP), GridWise Architecture Council (GWAC), and a network of experienced power system leaders, to develop a detailed outline of the path toward Transactive Energy.

It is immanently feasible to convert the entire United States by the year 2050. We think bellwether states, like California and Texas could be converted by 2025. The barriers are institutional, not physical or technical.

# The Transactive Energy Roadmap

The roadmap was developed in 2012 and the document is available at the website *www.cazalet.com* . It divides the future into four time periods:

1) 2013–15: **Introduction** of the Transactive Energy business model. This is a period of developing the TE vision, standards, and pilot demonstrations.

2) 2014–20: **Expansion**. A period of deployment of the TE business model on portions of the grid where value is high and there is regulatory and participant support.

3) 2015–30: **Hybrid.** A period of widespread deployment of TE within some regions with interfaces with existing operations and markets as needed.

4) 2020–50: **Mature.** This is the period when there is near full deployment of the TE business model within many regions.

The dates are ranges to indicate uncertainty in implementation—when various states and regions will begin each stage and how fast they will progress within each stage.

In each time period the roadmap describes developments in two categories:

1) **Grid Services**. Energy services will be offered in several categories: retail energy and distribution, ISO/ RTO (Independent System Operator/regional transmission operator) services, wholesale forward energy and transport services, and grid custodian services. In each category the stage-by-stage coordinated evolution of these services is described.

2) **Transactive Support Functions.** This category covers the gamut of activities needed to keep the physical and financial systems operating safely, reliably, and efficiently.

The roadmap also describes the function of each of the grid participants during each of the periods. This should be of particular interest to entrepreneurs who are waiting to jump at the "TE opportunity."

Based on the roadmap, it is realistic to think that California could complete the migration to TE in 10 years. The faster we convert, the earlier we realize the benefits.

The pace of change should be determined by the results of pilot projects. One of the tasks of the Stewardship Board will be to develop a specific roadmap for the IOUs and others in their service territories. Some regions and blocks of customers will be converted quicker than others. In California, the interim milestones should be set by the Stewardship Board and adjusted in response to results.

## Summary

A key takeaway from this roadmap is that TE can be transitioned smoothly from the current systems without a "big bang" change, such as when California previously tried restructuring of the markets on April 1, 1998.

SECTION 4

# Stewardship Board

## Overview

1. Only babies like to be changed.

2. Big, innovative changes require stewardship.

Innovation thrives when there is stewardship. This is especially true if the innovation is a new way of doing business in a long-established industry like electric power. Only babies like to be changed.

In the last decade, Californians have discovered a new mechanism for implementing policy changes: the Stewardship Board. The Board is empowered to implement policy and monitor changes. The approach has worked at least twice to implement highly visible policy with significant impacts.

The first application of the Stewardship Board was the Marine Life Protection Act (MLPA). This act directed the California Secretary of Resources to design and implement a network of marine protected areas along the entire coast of California. The Secretary of Natural Resources appointed a Blue Ribbon Task Force to act as the Stewardship Board.

The second application was the redrawing of the voter district lines statewide. This was done by a California Citizens Redistricting Commission.

Both MLPA and voter redistricting were implemented on schedule with massive stakeholder involvement and expert participation.

We believe this approach is appropriate for implementing the TE business model in California. The formation and composition of the Board would be directed by the legislature as in the case of the other "Boards" for the MLPA and voter redistricting. Responsibility for implementation of policy would ultimately rest with the governor.

In December 2012, the Little Hoover Commission Report, titled Rewiring California: Integrating Agendas for Energy Reform, recommended that the governor and the legislature should develop a plan to modernize energy governance. (*See www.lhc.ca.gov* .) The Commission recommended that careful consideration should be given to the establishment of a Secretary of Energy, reporting to the governor with all energy policy under one agency. Perhaps a TE Stewardship Board could be a part of that structure.

The implementation of the TE business model would seem to fit well into the structure recommended by the Little Hoover Commission. The Stewardship Board could be appointed by the Secretary of Energy or recruited according to a process set out by the legislature, as in the case of redistricting.

We will return to the TE implementation after reviewing how the network of marine reserves and the voter redistricting were accomplished.

## Designing a Network of Marine Protected Areas for California

California is a coastal state. The State has jurisdiction over the ocean within 3 miles off the coast. (Federal jurisdiction extends out to 200 miles.) In 1999 the California State legislature passed a law requiring establishment of a network of marine protected areas within state waters the length of the state. The Marine Life Protection Act (MLPA) established ecological and economic objectives for the network and also established a deadline for implementation.

The first attempts to involve scientists and stakeholders were supervised by the California Department of Fish and Game with the help of consultants. The effort stalled after 3 years because of lack of progress and money.

The State decided to restructure the MLPA implementation in 2004 after the disappointing first attempts. The new organization had three elements: a Blue Ribbon Task Force, a Stakeholder Interest Group, and a Science Advisory Team (see Figure 6-3). Each of these groups was supported by staff and consultants.

The Blue Ribbon Task Force was composed of eight members appointed by Mike Chrisman, the Secretary of the California Resources Agency:

> *This group represents a wide range of perspectives and is highly regarded for having good judgment. Their track record of results and breadth of experience in statewide and national policymaking is going to play a huge role in the success of this effort. This group has been assembled to look objectively at the history, the science related to marine protected areas, and the process to ensure that it remains open, will be accessible, and is considerate of all viewpoints. (For more detail on the creation of the Task Force, see the Memorandum of Understanding for California Marine Life Protection Act Initiative at the California Department of Wildlife website www.wildlife.ca.gov .)*

> *Quote from Mike Chrisman, Press Release, Feb. 22, 2007.*

The coast was divided into regions for purposes of planning. Each region had its own Stakeholder Interest Group recruited from within the region. Stakeholder Interest Group member recruitment was supervised by the Blue Ribbon Task Force.

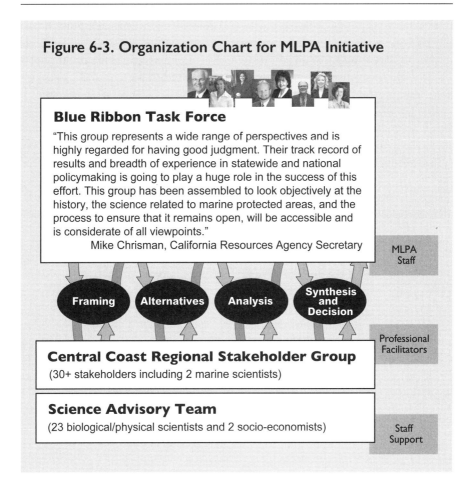

## Figure 6-3. Organization Chart for MLPA Initiative

**Blue Ribbon Task Force**

"This group represents a wide range of perspectives and is highly regarded for having good judgment. Their track record of results and breadth of experience in statewide and national policymaking is going to play a huge role in the success of this effort. This group has been assembled to look objectively at the history, the science related to marine protected areas, and the process to ensure that it remains open, will be accessible and is considerate of all viewpoints."

Mike Chrisman, California Resources Agency Secretary

MLPA Staff

Framing   Alternatives   Analysis   Synthesis and Decision

Professional Facilitators

**Central Coast Regional Stakeholder Group**

(30+ stakeholders including 2 marine scientists)

**Science Advisory Team**

(23 biological/physical scientists and 2 socio-economists)

Staff Support

The Science Advisory Panel was appointed by the Department of Fish and Game. It consisted of marine biologists, educators, and social scientists.

The Central Coast region, from Pilar Point on the north, to Point Conception on the south, was selected as the "pilot" region. The purpose was to protect one region at a time and carry forward lessons learned to subsequent regions.

The network design was completed on schedule and has been implemented. The network protects 850 square miles or 16.5% of California's ocean. Lessons learned from this effort are now being applied in developing a strategy for water management in the Sacramento River Delta of California.

Adequate funding was a key success factor for the MLPA project. State funds were supplemented by funds from nonprofit foundations like the Resource Legacy Fund. The funding allowed hiring highly qualified staff and conducting a huge community outreach and communication effort. Many public meetings were held up and down the state.

The key tenets of the MLPA Initiative were collaboration, stakeholder engagement, transparency, and science-based design. This proved to be a formula for success.

## Redrawing District Lines

The California Citizens Redistricting Commission is the second example of a "Stewardship Board" used to implement a difficult piece of legislation. Its mission was to redraw the lines that define voting districts throughout the state. Previously this was done by the legislature in a highly controversial political process and characterized by intense closed-door negotiation.

The Citizens Commission was authorized following the passage of California Proposition 11, the Voters First Act for Congress, by voters in November 2008. The Commission is responsible for determining the boundaries for the Senate, Assembly, and Board of Equalization districts in the state.

The 14-member commission consists of five Democrats, five Republicans, and four commissioners from neither major party. The commissioners were selected in November and December 2010 after a 1-year selection process. (The selection process was specified by the legislation.)

Following the 2008 passage of California Proposition 20, the Voters First Act for Congress, the Commission was assigned the responsibility of redrawing the state's U.S. congressional district boundaries in response to the congressional apportionment necessitated by the 2010 United States Census. The Commission was required to complete the new maps by August 15, 2011. They had 8 months to redraw all the state voter districts and complete the new redistricting.

As documented in its final report, the Commission engaged in an extensive public input process that included 34 hearings across the state where 2,700 citizens and a diverse range of organized groups gave public testimony, including organizations such as the League of Women Voters, California Forward, Common Cause, the California Chamber of Commerce (CalChamber), Equality

California, Mexican American Legal Defense and Educational Fund (MALDEF), the Asian Pacific American Legal Center, the National Association for the Advancement of Colored People (NAACP), the Silicon Valley Leadership Group, and the Sierra Club (for more information, see the California Citizens Redistricting Commission website at *wedrawthelines.ca.gov*).

This process differed from the past methods of redistricting in which "Historically, legislators drew the district boundaries in closed meetings, often favoring incumbents or their own party" (see the Frequently Asked Questions section of the *wedrawthelines.gov* website).

In contrast, the new Commission is independent and committed to including the voices of all Californians in the process. In addition to holding public hearings throughout the state, the Commission solicits citizen participation through its *wedrawthelines.gov* website as well as new media such as Twitter and Facebook. The Commissioners also participate in speaking engagements and educational forums throughout the state.

> *I'm proud that we were able to eliminate partisan gerrymandering and draw 177 districts for the state Assembly and Senate, Board of Equalization, and Congress on time and under budget.*
>
> *August 31, 2011, Cynthia Dai, Commission Chair*

The California redistricting effort demonstrates the power of a well-constituted Stewardship Board. The job of transforming California's electricity markets to the TE model seems manageable by comparison.

## How Should California Organize to Manage the Transition to TE?

We think an organizational structure parallel to the Marine Life Protection Act Initiative will be practical and efficient. The makeup of the Stewardship Board would be specified by the legislature. The possible mission statement might be similar to the following:

> This Board has been assembled to oversee the California State transition to a Transactive Energy business and regulatory model. The group represents a wide range of experts and perspectives that represent both professional and private interests. The participants have

been chosen because of their track record of results and breadth of experience in statewide and national policymaking.

Much of the work of the Board would be carried out by two groups: a Stakeholder Group and a Science and Engineering Team (see Figure 6-4).

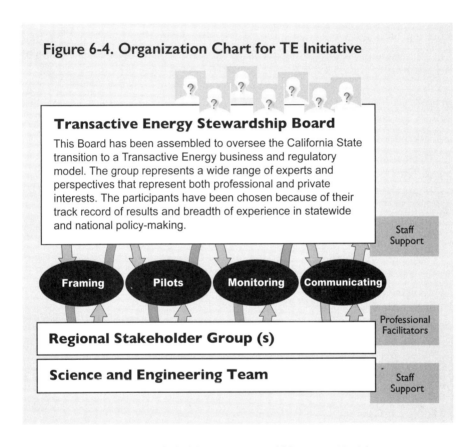

## Figure 6-4. Organization Chart for TE Initiative

**Transactive Energy Stewardship Board**

This Board has been assembled to oversee the California State transition to a Transactive Energy business and regulatory model. The group represents a wide range of experts and perspectives that represent both professional and private interests. The participants have been chosen because of their track record of results and breadth of experience in statewide and national policy-making.

Framing · Pilots · Monitoring · Communicating

Staff Support

**Regional Stakeholder Group (s)**

**Science and Engineering Team**

Professional Facilitators

Staff Support

As with the MLPA, the Stakeholder Group would be 20 to 30 citizens representing the cross section of special interests involved in energy production and consumption. They would be selected from the general population by a transparent and fair process. This group's activities would be facilitated by professional facilitators. Their job would be to raise issues, provide information, and express the values of their constituencies. (Knowledgeable stakeholders who have direct interest in energy are the heart and soul of the process.)

The Science and Engineering Team has the responsibility to provide evidence-based expertise on social science, economics, and technology. The members of this group would probably be appointed by the Secretary of Energy.

## Summary

There are many ways to form and implement policy. The Stewardship Board concept may be the first consideration for implementing the TE business and regulatory model. It offers a balance of authority, participation, and rigorous science, and has a proven track record.

CHAPTER 7

# Our Basis for Writing This Book

**Stephen Barrager, Ph.D.**      **Edward Cazalet, Ph.D**

Both Stephen Barrager and Edward Cazalet are pioneers in the development of the modern electric power system. They have made groundbreaking contributions to electric power research and development. This chapter offers a short statement of qualifications for each author.

## Stephen M. Barrager, Ph.D.

Dr. Stephen Barrager is the founder and publisher of Baker Street Publishing. He lectures on organizational decision-making and environmental decision-making at Stanford University. He is currently writing about the science and engineering of organizational decisions.

In the 1980s, Barrager worked with the Electric Power Research Institute to develop the first integrated planning models and methods for the electric power industry. The models have been used worldwide to support demand-side decision-making. Companies that used the models account for two-thirds of the electricity produced in the United States. He was a cofounder of Decision Focus, Incorporated, and the founder and CEO of Electric Power Software.

He has worked on a broad range of energy and environmental policy issues. He was the chair of the Science Advisory Team and the Leadership Team for the California Marine Life Protection Act Initiative. This highly successful Initiative established a network of marine protected areas across the California coast. He has held several appointments with the Pacific Fisheries Management Council.

Previously he was a director and board member at Strategic Decisions Group (SDG) in Palo Alto, California. During his years with SDG, Barrager led a major 8-year engagement with General Motors. The goal of the program was to upgrade strategic decision-making throughout the company. The range of major decision areas included business innovation, product planning, branding, marketing and sales strategy, global sourcing strategy, research and development (R&D) planning, and environmental strategy. The results of most of this work are embodied in the "New GM."

Barrager has worked in a wide variety of business sectors: aerospace, computers, automobile and chemical industries, electronics, mining, transportation, food, and energy. He has facilitated many senior executive workshops and taught strategic decision-making and R&D planning for executives. He has led multidisciplinary, multinational teams in Asia, Europe, South America, and the Middle East.

Dr. Barrager holds a Ph.D. from Stanford University where he focused on decision analysis, economics, and ecology. He has an engineering degree from Northwestern University.

# Edward G. Cazalet, Ph.D.

Dr. Edward Cazalet is a leader in the design and operation of markets for electricity, the design and operation of smart grid transaction services, electricity storage, and renewables integration. For his industry contributions, Public Utilities Fortnightly magazine named Dr. Cazalet Innovator of the Year.

Cazalet is the founder and CEO of TeMix Inc., a global transactive systems company. He was previously a governor of the California Independent System Operator (CAISO) and is the founder or cofounder of MegaWatt Storage, Farms, Automated Power Exchange (APX), Decision Focus, Inc., and The Cazalet Group.

Dr. Cazalet is a leader in applying technology to automate electric power transactions. He has extensive experience in designing, building, and operating high-speed, reliable transaction systems for electric power that interface with legacy transaction systems and markets.

He is co-chair of the Energy Market Information Exchange's (EMIX) Technical Committee for the Organization for Advancement of Structured Information Standards (OASIS), and is the author of the Committee's white paper on the Transactive Energy Market Information (TeMix) standards.

As a governor of the CAISO, Dr. Cazalet served as transition manager–interim CEO while the search for a permanent CEO of the CAISO was completed. He also served as vice chair of the board and chair of the Operations Committee. He oversaw market design, resource adequacy, market and grid operations, and transmission planning. In addition, he oversaw the design and implementation of the multi-hundred million dollar project for new software and hardware for the CAISO locational marginal price (LMP) markets.

As chairman and CEO of APX he raised almost $70 million in three rounds from venture capital investors and strategic power industry investors, such as Bechtel, Tokyo Electric, Kyushu Electric, Hydro Quebec, Exelon, and First Energy. He successfully led the company into diverse power exchange, scheduling, demand response, and settlements businesses in North America, Europe, and Asia. APX operated the first green power exchange market and became the leader in renewable and carbon registries.

For 40 years, Dr. Cazalet has been active in state and federal energy policy debates, including synthetic fuels, natural gas deregulation, electric power generation, transmission planning, and electricity storage. He was the initial advocate for California's "Energy Storage Systems" mandate known as the bill AB 2514.

Cazalet holds a Ph.D. from Stanford University where he focused on decision analysis, economics, and power systems. He also has degrees in engineering from the University of Washington.

# Glossary

## ANSI

The Institute oversees the creation, promulgation and use of thousands of norms and guidelines that directly impact businesses in nearly every sector: from acoustical devices to construction equipment, from dairy and livestock production to energy distribution, and many more.

Source: ANSI Website *www.ansi.org*

## Apps

Application software is a set of one or more programs designed to carry out operations for a specific application. Application software cannot run on itself but it is dependent on system software to execute. For example: MS Word, MS Excel, Tally software, Library management system, billing system, etc.

The term is used to contrast such software with another type of computer program referred to as system software, which manages and integrates a computer's capabilities but does not directly perform tasks that benefit the user. The system software serves the application, which in turn serves the user.

Examples include accounting software, enterprise software, graphics software, media players, and office suites. Many application programs deal principally with documents. Applications may be bundled with the computer and its system software or published separately, and can be coded as university projects.

Application software applies the power of a particular computing platform or system software to a particular purpose.

From Wikipedia, the Free Encyclopedia

## Capital Stock

In economics, capital stock or physical capital refers to a factor of production (or input into the process of production), such as machinery, buildings, or computers. In the electricity ecosystem it is the generators, industrial equipment, storage units, buildings, appliances, and vehicles. Generally it is all the things you can kick. It is the things that are part of the physical assets of a company

## CHP (Combined Heat and Power)

Cogeneration or combined heat and power (CHP) is the use of a heat engine or power station to simultaneously generate electricity and useful heat.

Cogeneration is a thermodynamically efficient use of fuel. In separate production of electricity, some energy must be discarded as waste heat, but in cogeneration this thermal energy is put to use. All thermal power plants emit heat during electricity generation, which can be released into the natural environment through cooling towers, flue gas, or by other means. In contrast, CHP captures some or all of the byproduct for heating, either very close to the plant, or—especially in Scandinavia and Eastern Europe—as hot water for district heating with temperatures ranging from approximately 80 to 130 °C. This is also called combined heat and power district heating (CHPDH). Small CHP plants are an example of decentralized energy. Byproduct heat at moderate temperatures (100–180 °C, 212–356 °F) can also be used in absorption refrigerators for cooling.

In CHP installations the supply of high-temperature heat first drives a gas or steam turbine-powered generator and the resulting low-temperature waste heat is then used for water or space heating. At smaller scales (typically below 1 MW) a gas engine or diesel engine may be used.

Cogeneration was practiced in some of the earliest installations of electrical generation. Before central stations distributed power, industries generating their own power used exhaust steam for process heating. Large office and apartment buildings, hotels and stores commonly generated their own power and used waste steam for building heat. Due to the high cost of early purchased power, these CHP operations continued for many years after utility electricity became available.

Cogeneration is still common in pulp and paper mills, refineries and chemical plants. In this "industrial cogeneration/CHP", the heat is typically recovered at higher temperatures (above 100 deg C) and used for process steam or drying duties. This is more valuable and flexible than low-grade waste heat, but there is a slight loss of power generation. The increased focus on sustainability has made industrial CHP more attractive, as it substantially reduces carbon footprint compared to generating steam or burning fuel on-site and importing electric power from the grid.

## Cloud

Cloud computing involves computing over a network, where a program or application may run on many connected computers at the same time. It specifically refers to a computing hardware machine or group of computing hardware machines commonly referred as a server connected through a communication network such as the Internet, an intranet, a local area network (LAN) or wide area network (WAN). Any individual user who has permission to access the server can use the server's processing power to run an application, store data, or perform any other computing task. Therefore, instead of using a personal computer every-time to run the application, the individual can now run the application from anywhere in the world, as the server provides the processing power to the application and the server is also connected to a network via internet or other connection platforms to be accessed from anywhere. All this has become possible due to increasing computer processing power available to humankind with decrease in cost as stated in Moore's law.

In common usage the term "the cloud" is essentially a metaphor for the Internet. Marketers have further popularized the phrase "in the cloud" to refer to software, platforms and infrastructure that are sold "as a service", i.e. remotely through the Internet. Typically, the seller has actual energy-consuming servers which host products and services from a remote location, so end-users don't have to; they can simply log on to the network without installing anything. The major models of cloud computing service are known as software as a service, platform as a service, and infrastructure as a service. These cloud services may be offered in a public, private or hybrid network. Google, Amazon, IBM, Oracle Cloud, Rackspace, Salesforce, Zoho and Microsoft Azure are some well-known cloud vendors.

Network-based services, which appear to be provided by real server hardware and are in fact served up by virtual hardware simulated by software running on one or more real machines, are often called cloud computing. Such virtual servers do not physically exist and can therefore be moved around and scaled up or down on the fly without affecting the end user, somewhat like a cloud becoming larger or smaller without being a physical object.

## Decentralized Energy Resources (DER's

Distributed generation, also called on-site generation, dispersed generation, embedded generation, decentralized generation, decentralized energy, distributed energy or district energy,[1] generates electricity from many small energy sources. Most countries generate electricity in large centralized facilities, such as fossil fuel (coal, gas powered), nuclear, large solar power plants or hydropower plants. These plants have excellent economies of scale, but usually transmit electricity long distances and can negatively affect the environment. Distributed generation allows collection of energy from many sources and may give lower environmental impacts and improved security of supply.

Types of distributed energy resources include the following:

Cogeneration. Distributed cogeneration sources use steam turbines, natural gas-fired fuel cells, micro turbines or reciprocating engines to turn generators. The hot exhaust is then used for space or water heating, or to drive an absorptive chiller for cooling such as air-conditioning. In addition to natural gas-based schemes, distributed energy projects can also include other renewable or low carbon fuels including biofuels, biogas, landfill gas, sewage gas, coal bed methane, syngas and associated petroleum gas.

Solar panels. Popular sources of power for distributed generation are photovoltaic solar panels and heat collection panels on the roofs of buildings or frcc-standing.

Wind turbines. Small wind turbines have low maintenance, and low pollution.

Vehicle-to-grid. Future generations of electric vehicles may have the ability to deliver power from the battery in a vehicle-to-grid into the grid when needed. An electric vehicle network could also be an important distributed generation resource.

Waste-to-energy. Municipal solid waste (MSW) and natural waste, such as sewage sludge, food waste and animal manure will decompose and discharge methane containing gas that can be collected as used as fuel in gas turbines or micro turbines to produce electricity as a distributed energy resource.

# DLC

Direct load control (DLC) refers to the scenario where third party entities outside the home or facility are responsible for deciding how and when specific customer loads will be controlled in response to Demand Response (DR) events on the electric grid. Examples of third parties responsible for performing DLC may be Utilities, Independent System Operators (ISO), Aggregators, or third party control companies. DLC can be contrasted with facility centric load control (FCLC) where the decisions for how loads are controlled are made entirely within the facility or enterprise control systems. In FCLC the facility owner has more freedom of choice in how to respond to DR events on the grid. Both approaches are in use today in automation of DR.

From Berkeley Lab

## EI (Energy Interoperation)

Energy Interoperation (EI) supports the following:

• Transactive Energy

• Distribution of dynamic and contract prices

• Demand response approaches ranging from dispatch of load resources to price levels embedded in an event.

• Measurement and confirmation of response.

• Projected price, demand, and energy

EI engages Distributed Energy Resources (DER) while making no assumptions as to their processes or technology.

While this specification supports agreements and transactional obligations, this specification offers flexibility of implementation to support specific programs, regional requirements, and goals of the various participants including the utility industry, aggregators, suppliers, and device manufacturers.

It is not the intent of the Energy Interoperation Technical Committee to imply that any particular agreements are endorsed, proposed, or required in order to implement this specification. Energy market operations are beyond the scope of this specification although the interactions that enable management of the actual delivery and acceptance are within scope. Energy Interoperation defines interfaces for use throughout the transport chain of electricity as well as supporting today's intermediation services and that may arise tomorrow.

Source: OASIS website, *https://www.oasis-open.org*

## EMIX (Energy Market Information Exchange)

Energy markets and sales have been characterized by tariffs and embedded knowledge that make decision automation difficult. Smart grids introduce rapidly changing products and product availability, with associated dynamic prices. Lack of standardized messages conveying a standardized vocabulary for market information has been a barrier to development and deployment of technology to respond to changing market circumstances.

Price and product definition are actionable information. When presented with standard messages conveying price and product, automated systems can make decisions to optimize energy and economic results. In regulated electricity markets, price and products often are defined by complex tariffs, derived through political processes. EMIX defines the information for use in messages that convey this actionable information. An essential distinction between energy and other markets is that price is strongly influenced by time of delivery. EMIX conveys time and interval by incorporating WS-Calendar into tenders, contracts, and performance calls.

**An essential distinction between energy and other markets is that price is strongly influenced by time of delivery.** Energy for sale at 2:00 AM, when energy use is low, is not the same price as energy for sale at the same location at 2:00 PM, during the working day. EMIX conveys time and interval by incorporating WS-Calendar into tenders, contracts, and performance calls.

Not all market information is available in real time. Present day markets, particularly wholesale markets, may have deferred charges (e.g. balancing charges) that cannot be determined at point of sale. Other markets may require additional purchases to allow the use of the energy purchased (e.g. same-time transmission rights or pipeline fees when accepting delivery on a forward contract). EMIX is useful for representing available price and product information.

Source: OASIS website, *https://www.oasis-open.org*

## EMS (Energy Management System)

The term Energy Management System (EMS) generally refers to a computer system which is designed specifically for the automated control and monitoring of those electromechanical facilities in a building which yield significant energy consumption such as heating, ventilation and lighting installations. The scope may span from a single building to a group of buildings such as university campuses, office buildings, retail stores networks or factories. Most of these energy management systems also provide facilities for the reading of electricity, gas and water meters. The data obtained from these can then be used to perform self-diagnostic and optimization routines on a frequent basis and to produce trend analysis and annual consumption forecasts.

Historically, energy management system (EMS) is a system of computer-aided tools used by operators of electric utility grids to monitor, control, and optimize the performance of the generation and/or transmission system.

EMS's are currently being embedded into home thermostats, smart appliances, and electric vehicles. These systems can be monitored and controlled remotely using smart phones. The devices can monitor any information available in the Cloud or from wireless devices in the home. Their control algorithms can be embedded in the device or accessed via the internet.

From Wikipedia

## Energy

In physics, energy is a property of objects, transferable among them via fundamental interactions, which can be converted in form but not created or destroyed. The joule is the standard unit of energy, based on the amount transferred to an object by the mechanical work of moving it one metre against a force of one newton.

Work and heat are two categories of processes or mechanisms that can transfer a given amount of energy. The second law of thermodynamics limits the amount of work that can be performed by energy that is obtained via a heating process—some energy is always lost as waste heat. The maximum amount that can go into work is called the available energy. Systems such as machines and living things often require available energy, not just any energy. Mechanical and other forms of energy can be transformed in the other direction into thermal energy without such limitations.

From Wikipedia, the free encyclopedia

## FIX (Financial Information Exchange Protocol)

The Financial Information eXchange (FIX) protocol is an electronic communications protocol initiated in 1992 for international real-time exchange of information related to the securities transactions and markets. With trillions of dollars traded annually on the NASDAQ alone, financial service entities are investing heavily in optimizing electronic trading and employing direct market access (DMA) to increase their speed to financial markets. Managing the delivery of trading applications and keeping latency low increasingly requires an understanding of the FIX protocol.

From Wikipedia, the free encyclopedia

## Fracking

Fracking, or hydraulic fracturing, is forcing fractures in a rock layer, by pressurized fluid. It can happen naturally, but it is now used to force oil and natural gas from shale.

Some hydraulic fractures form naturally: certain dykes are examples. This lets gas and petroleum from source rocks get to reservoir rocks.

The first use of hydraulic fracturing was in 1947. The modern fracturing technique, called 'horizontal slickwater fracturing', was first used in 1998. It made the extraction of shale gas economical. The energy from the injection of a highly pressurized fluid creates new channels in the rock, which increases the extraction rates and recovery of hydrocarbons. In 2010 it was estimated that 60% of all new oil and gas wells worldwide were being hydraulically fractured. As of 2012, 2.5 million hydraulic fracturing jobs have been performed on oil and gas wells worldwide, more than one million of them in the United States.

from Wikipedia, the free encyclopedia

## Gigawatt

The gigawatt is equal to one billion watts or one gigawatt = 1000 megawatts. This unit is sometimes used for large power plants or power grids. For example, by the end of 2010 power shortages in China's Shanxi province were expected to increase to 5–6 GW and the installed capacity of wind power in Germany was

25.8 GW. The largest unit (out of four) of the Belgian Nuclear Plant Doel has a peak output of 1.04 GW. The London Array, the world's largest offshore wind farm, is designed to produce a gigawatt of power.

From Wikipedia, the free encyclopedia

## Grid

An electrical grid (also referred to as an electricity grid or electric grid) is an interconnected network for delivering electricity from suppliers to consumers. It consists of generating stations that produce electrical power, high-voltage transmission lines that carry power from distant sources to demand centers, and distribution lines that connect individual customers.

Power stations may be located near a fuel source, at a dam site, or to take advantage of renewable energy sources, and are often located away from heavily populated areas. They are usually quite large to take advantage of the economies of scale. The electric power which is generated is stepped up to a higher voltage-at which it connects to the transmission network.

The transmission network will move the power long distances, sometimes across international boundaries, until it reaches its wholesale customer (usually the company that owns the local distribution network).

On arrival at a substation, the power will be stepped down from a transmission level voltage to a distribution level voltage. As it exits the substation, it enters the distribution wiring. Finally, upon arrival at the service location, the power is stepped down again from the distribution voltage to the required service voltage(s).

From Wikipedia, the free encyclopedia

## ICT

Information and communications technology (ICT) is often used as an extended synonym for information technology (IT), but is a more specific term that stresses the role of unified communications and the integration of telecommunications (telephone lines and wireless signals), computers as well as necessary enterprise software, middleware, storage, and audio-visual systems, which enable users to access, store, transmit, and manipulate information.

The phrase ICT had been used by academic researchers since the 1980s, but it became popular after it was used in a report to the UK government by Dennis Stevenson in 1997 and in the revised National Curriculum for England, Wales and Northern Ireland in 2000. As of September 2013, the term "ICT" in the UK National Curriculum has been replaced by the broader term "computing".

The term ICT is now also used to refer to the convergence of audio-visual and telephone networks with computer networks through a single cabling or link system. There are large economic incentives (huge cost savings due to elimination of the telephone network) to merge the telephone network with the computer network system using a single unified system of cabling, signal distribution and management.

From Wikipedia, the free encyclopedia

## Intermediaries

There are three primary groups of parties in a TE system: Energy Service Parties, Transport Services Parties, and Intermediaries. Energy Services Parties can be customers, producers, prosumers, or storage owners. Transport Services Parties are transmission or distribution owners. The intermediaries include exchanges, market makers, retailers and system operators See Figure 1-8.

## IOU

An investor-owned utility or IOU is a business organization, providing a product or service regarded as a utility (often termed a public utility regardless of ownership), and managed as private enterprise rather than a function of government or a utility cooperative. Such businesses can range from a family whose residential property includes a well whose flow in excess of the family's own needs produces a secondary income, to international communications conglomerates, but political and infrastructure considerations in some countries makes the private sector of the electric-power production and distribution industry the most often discussed investor-owned utilities there.

In the United States of America, public utilities are often natural monopolies because the infrastructure required to produce and deliver a product such as electricity or water is very expensive to build and maintain. As a result, they are often government monopolies, or if privately owned, the sectors are specially regulated by a public utilities commission.

Developments in technology have eroded some of the natural monopoly aspects of traditional public utilities. For instance, electricity generation, electricity retailing, telecommunication, some types of public transit and postal services have become competitive in some countries and the trend towards liberalization, deregulation and privatization of public utilities is growing, but the network infrastructure used to distribute most utility products and services has remained largely monopolistic.

Public utilities can be privately owned or publicly owned. Publicly owned utilities include cooperative and municipal utilities. Municipal utilities may actually include territories outside of city limits or may not even serve the entire city. Cooperative utilities are owned by the customers they serve. They are usually found in rural areas. Private utilities, also called investor-owned utilities, are owned by investors.

From Wikipedia, the free encyclopedia

## ISO

In California the Independent System Operator is CAISO. The CAISO oversees the operation of California's bulk electric power system, transmission lines, and electricity market generated and transmitted by its member utilities. The primary stated mission of the CAISO is to "operate the grid reliably and efficiently, provide fair and open transmission access, promote environmental stewardship, and facilitate effective markets and promote infrastructure development." The CAISO is one of the largest ISOs in the world, delivering 300 million megawatt-hours of electricity each year and managing about 80% of California's electric flow.

CAISO was created in 1998 when the state restructured its electricity markets at the recommendation of the Federal Energy Regulatory Commission (FERC), following the passage of the federal Energy Policy Act of 1992, which removed barriers to competition in the wholesale generation of the electricity business. The CAISO is regulated by the FERC because interstate transmission lines fall under the jurisdiction of federal commerce laws.

From Wikipedia, the free encyclopedia

## kW

The kilowatt is equal to one thousand watts. This unit is typically used to express the output power of engines and the power of electric motors, tools, machines, and heaters.

In the USA and some other countries, one kilowatt is approximately equal to 1.34 horsepower. A small electric heater with one heating element can use one kilowatt, which is equivalent to the power of a household in the United States averaged over the entire year.

A surface area of one square meter on Earth receives typically one kilowatt of sunlight from the sun (on a clear day at mid day).

From Wikipedia, the free encyclopedia

## kWh

The kilowatt hour, or kilowatt-hour, (symbol kW•h, kW h or kWh) is a unit of energy equal to 1,000 watt-hours, or 3.6 megajoules.[1][2] If the energy is being transmitted or used at a constant rate (power) over a period of time, the total energy in kilowatt-hours is the product of the power in kilowatts and the time in hours. The kilowatt-hour is commonly used as a billing unit for energy delivered to consumers by electric utilities.

A heater rated at 1000 watts (one kilowatt), operating for one hour uses one kilowatt-hour of energy. A 60-watt light bulb operating for 100 hours uses 6 kilowatt-hours. Electrical energy is sold in kilowatt-hours; cost of running equipment is the product of power in kilowatts multiplied by running time in hours and price per kilowatt-hour. The unit price of electricity may depend upon the rate of consumption and the time of day. Industrial users may also have extra charges according to their peak usage and the power factor.

From Wikipedia, the free encyclopedia

## Marginal Cost

In economics and finance, marginal cost is the change in the total cost that arises when the quantity produced is increased by one unit. That is, it is the cost of producing one more unit of a good.

In general terms, marginal cost at each level of production includes any additional costs required to produce the next unit. For example, if producing additional vehicles requires building a new factory, the marginal cost of the extra vehicles includes the cost of the new factory. In practice, this analysis is segregated into short- and long-run cases, so that over the longest run, all costs become marginal. At each level of production and time period being considered, marginal costs include all costs that vary with the level of production, whereas other costs that do not vary with production are considered fixed.

From Wikipedia, the free encyclopedia

## Market Maker

In Transactive Energy (TE) market makers stand ready to simultaneously buy or sell energy or transport by posting tenders at specific locations (or location pairs for transport) and specific forward intervals.

Market makers frequently post small buy and sell tenders with short expiration times. Market makers will accumulate a long or short inventory position as counter parties accept their tenders. When a market maker has a long position he will decrease the prices of subsequent buy and sell tenders; when a market maker has a short position he will increase the prices of subsequent buy and sell positions. Most market makers will use automated market making algorithms.

Market makers are important to TE because they provide forward tenders that buyers and sellers and their automated energy management systems (EMS) can act on and execute forward transactions.

In the TE model other parties in addition to market makers can post tenders. Parties will generally transact with counter parties including market makers that offer the best priced tenders.

It is likely that regulators will oversee market makers. Market makers may make or lose money and may play a significant role in market stability.

## Megawatt

The megawatt is equal to one million watts. Many events or machines produce or sustain the conversion of energy on this scale, including lightning strikes; large electric motors; large warships such as aircraft carriers, cruisers, and submarines; large server farms or data centers; and some scientific research equipment, such as super-colliders, and the output pulses of very large lasers. A large residential or commercial building may use several megawatts in electric power and heat. On railways, modern high-powered electric locomotives typically have a peak power output of 5 or 6 MW, although some produce much more. The Eurostar, for example, uses more than 12 MW, while heavy diesel-electric locomotives typically produce/use 3 to 5 MW. U.S. nuclear power plants have net summer capacities between about 500 and 1300 MW.

From Wikipedia, the free encyclopedia

## Microgrid

A microgrid is a localized grouping of electricity generation, energy storage, and loads that normally operates connected to a traditional centralized grid (macrogrid). This single point of common coupling with the macrogrid can be disconnected. The microgrid can then function autonomously. Generation and loads in a microgrid are usually interconnected at low voltage. From the point of view of the grid operator, a connected microgrid can be controlled as if it were one entity.

Microgrid generation resources can include fuel cells, wind, solar, or other energy sources. The multiple dispersed generation sources and ability to isolate the microgrid from a larger network would provide highly reliable electric power. Produced heat from generation sources such as microturbines could be used for local process heating or space heating, allowing flexible trade off between the needs for heat and electric power.

From Wikipedia, the free encyclopedia

## Moore's Law

Moore's law is the observation that, over the history of computing hardware, the number of transistors on integrated circuits doubles approximately every two years. The law is named after Gordon E. Moore, co-founder of Intel Corporation, who described the trend in his 1965 paper. His prediction has proven to be accurate, in part because the law is now used in the semiconductor industry to guide long-term planning and to set targets for research and development. The capabilities of many digital electronic devices are strongly linked to Moore's law: processing speed, memory capacity, sensors and even the number and size of pixels in digital cameras. All of these are improving at roughly exponential rates as well. This exponential improvement has dramatically enhanced the impact of digital electronics in nearly every segment of the world economy. Moore's law describes a driving force of technological and social change in the late 20th and early 21st centuries.

The period is often quoted as 18 months because of Intel executive David House, who predicted that chip performance would double every 18 months (being a combination of the effect of more transistors and their being faster).

Although this trend has continued for more than half a century, Moore's law should be considered an observation or conjecture and not a physical or natural law. Sources in 2005 expected it to continue until at least 2015 or 2020. However, the 2010 update to the International Technology Roadmap for Semiconductors predicted that growth will slow at the end of 2013, when transistor counts and densities are to double only every three years.

From Wikipedia, the free encyclopedia

## MRID

Master Resource ID This specification defines an approach for globally providing and formulating unambiguous reference designations for Electrical Power System objects defined within the EPRI Common Information Model (CIM). This document initially defines the requirements for a unique identifier for a Substation but is not limited to the CIM class of Substations. Other objects, defined within the CIM, could have unique identifiers if needed.

From Wikipedia, the free encyclopedia

## NERC

The North American Electric Reliability Corporation (NERC) is a not-for-profit international regulatory authority whose mission is to ensure the reliability of the bulk power system in North America. NERC develops and enforces Reliability Standards; annually assesses seasonal and long-term reliability; monitors the bulk power system through system awareness; and educates, trains, and certifies industry personnel. NERC's area of responsibility spans the continental United States, Canada, and the northern portion of Baja California, Mexico. NERC is the electric reliability organization for North America, subject to oversight by the Federal Energy Regulatory Commission and governmental authorities in Canada. NERC's jurisdiction includes users, owners, and operators of the bulk power system, which serves more than 334 million people.

From NERC website, *http://www.nerc.com*

## Net Metering

Net metering is a service to an electric consumer under which electric energy generated by that electric consumer from an eligible on-site generating facility and delivered to the local distribution facilities may be used to offset electric energy provided by the electric utility to the electric consumer during the applicable billing period.

Net metering policies can vary significantly by country and by state or province: if net metering is available, if and how long you can keep your banked credits, and how much the credits are worth (retail/wholesale). Most net metering laws involve monthly roll over of kWh credits, a small monthly connection fee, require monthly payment of deficits (i.e. normal electric bill), and annual settlement of any residual credit. Unlike a feed-in tariff (FIT) or time of use metering (TOU), net metering can be implemented solely as an accounting procedure, and requires no special metering, or even any prior arrangement or notification.

Net metering is a policy designed to foster private investment in renewable energy. In the United States, as part of the Energy Policy Act of 2005, all public electric utilities are required to make available upon request net metering to their customers.

From Wikipedia, the free encyclopedia

## Net Present Value

In finance, the net present value (NPV) of a time series of cash flows, both incoming and outgoing, is defined as the sum of the present values (PVs) of the individual cash flows of the same entity.

In the case when all future cash flows are incoming (such as coupons and principal of a bond) and the only outflow of cash is the purchase price, the NPV is simply the PV of future cash flows minus the purchase price (which is its own PV). NPV is a central tool in discounted cash flow (DCF) analysis and is a standard method for using the time value of money to appraise long-term projects. Used for capital budgeting and widely used throughout economics, finance, and accounting, it measures the excess or shortfall of cash flows, in present value terms, above the cost of funds.

NPV can be described as the "difference amount" between the sums of discounted cash inflows and cash outflows. It compares the present value of money today to the present value of money in the future, taking inflation and returns into account.

From Wikipedia, the free encyclopedia

## NIST

Founded in 1901 and now part of the U.S. Department of Commerce, NIST is one of the nation's oldest physical science laboratories. Congress established the agency to remove a major handicap to U.S. industrial competitiveness at the time—a second-rate measurement infrastructure that lagged behind the capabilities of England, Germany, and other economic rivals. Today, NIST measurements support the smallest of technologies—nanoscale devices so tiny that tens of thousands can fit on the end of a single human hair—to the largest and most complex of human-made creations, from earthquake-resistant skyscrapers to wide-body jetliners to global communication networks.

From NIST website, *http://www.nist.gov*

## OASIS

OASIS (Advancing Open Standards for the Information Society) is a non-profit consortium that drives the development, convergence and adoption of open standards for the global information society.

OASIS promotes industry consensus and produces worldwide standards for security, Internet of Things, cloud computing, energy, content technologies, emergency management, and other areas. OASIS open standards offer the potential to lower cost, stimulate innovation, grow global markets, and protect the right of free choice of technology.

OASIS members broadly represent the marketplace of public and private sector technology leaders, users and influencers. The consortium has more than 5,000 participants representing over 600 organizations and individual members in more than 65 countries.

OASIS is distinguished by its transparent governance and operating procedures. Members themselves set the OASIS technical agenda, using a lightweight process expressly designed to promote industry consensus and unite disparate efforts. Completed work is ratified by open ballot. Governance is accountable and unrestricted. Officers of both the OASIS Board of Directors and Technical Advisory Board are chosen by democratic election to serve two-year terms. Consortium leadership is based on individual merit and is not tied to financial contribution, corporate standing, or special appointment.

From OASIS website, *https://www.oasis-open.org*

## Party

A party is a person, family or entity. Instances of a party include a metered end customer, prosumer, generator, or storage operator, an electric vehicle owner, distribution operator, transmission operator, system operator, an exchange operator , market maker, retailer or marketer.

## PayPal

PayPal is an international e-commerce business allowing payments and money transfers to be made through the Internet. Online money transfers serve as electronic alternatives to paying with traditional paper methods, such as checks and money orders. It is subject to the US economic sanction list, and subject to other rules and interventions required by US laws or government.

PayPal is an acquirer, performing payment processing for online vendors, auction sites, and other commercial users, for which it charges a fee. The fee depends on what currency or payments the seller is using. In addition, eBay purchases made by credit card through PayPal may incur extra fees if the buyer and seller use different currencies.

On October 3, 2002, PayPal became a wholly owned subsidiary of eBay. Its corporate headquarters are in San Jose, California, United States. The company also has significant operations in Omaha, Scottsdale, Charlotte, Boston, Baltimore and Austin in the United States; Chennai and Bangalore in India; Dublin and Dundalk in Ireland; Kleinmachnow in Germany; and Tel Aviv in Israel.

From Wikipedia, the free encyclopedia

## Peer-to-Peer

A peer-to-peer (P2P) network is a type of decentralized and distributed network architecture in which individual nodes in the network (called "peers") act as both suppliers and consumers of resources, in contrast to centralized client–server model where client nodes request access to resources provided by central servers.

In the TE model, a peer-to-peer transaction between two consumers or prosumers is an example of a peer-to-peer transaction.

From Wikipedia, the free encyclopedia

## Power

Electric power is the rate at which electric energy is transferred by an electric circuit. The unit of power is the watt, one joule per second.

Electric power is usually produced by electric generators, but can also be supplied by sources such as electric batteries. Electric power is generally supplied to businesses and homes by the electric power industry. Electric power is usually sold by the kilowatt hour which is the product of power in kilowatts multiplied by running time in hours. Electric utilities measure power using an electricity meter, which keeps a running total of the electric energy delivered to a customer.

From Wikipedia, the free encyclopedia

## Prosumer

Prosumer is a portmanteau originally formed by contracting producer with the word consumer. In a commercial environment, it describes a market segment between producer and consumer. For example, a residential electricity customer with PV panels can both consume and produce electricity.

From Wikipedia, the free encyclopedia

## PV panels

A Rooftop photovoltaic power station is a system which uses one or more photovoltaic panels, installed on rooftops of residential or commercial buildings, to convert sunlight into electricity. The various components in a rooftop photovoltaic power station include photovoltaic modules, mounting systems, cables, Solar inverters and other electrical accessories

## Rate Base

The rate base is the book value, after depreciation, of the generation, distribution and transmission infrastructure owned and operated by the utility. Utilities earn a regulated rate of return on their rate base. Other things being equal, a larger rate base results in higher net income for the utilities (and vice versa). As assets are depreciated over time, the rate base declines. Rate base increases when utilities build new plant and infrastructure or make capital additions and improvements. Changes in rate base also result in changes in the depreciation allowance utilities are authorized to collect. Between 2003 and 2011, the [California] utilities' rate base increased from $22 billion to $39 billion, leading to increases in GRC revenue requirements.

From California Public Utility Commission Cost report 2011,
*http://www.cpuc.ca.gov/NR/rdonlyres/1C5DC9A9-3440-43EA-9C61-065FAD1FD111/0/AB67CostReport201.pdf*

## Regulators

A regulatory agency (also regulatory authority, regulatory body or regulator) is a public authority or government agency responsible for exercising autonomous authority over some area of human activity in a regulatory or supervisory capacity. An independent regulatory agency is a regulatory agency that is independent from other branches or arms of the government.

Regulatory agencies deal in the area of administrative law—regulation or rule-making (codifying and enforcing rules and regulations and imposing supervision or oversight for the benefit of the public at large).The existence of independent regulatory agencies is justified by the complexity of certain regulatory and supervisory tasks that require expertise, the need for rapid implementation of public authority in certain sectors, and the drawbacks of political interference. Some independent regulatory agencies perform investigations or audits, and some are authorized to fine the relevant parties and order certain measures.

Regulatory agencies are usually a part of the executive branch of the government, or they have statutory authority to perform their functions with oversight from the legislative branch.Their actions are generally open to legal review. Regulatory authorities are commonly set up to enforce standards and safety, or to oversee use of public goods and regulate commerce. Examples of regulatory agencies are the Interstate Commerce Commission and U.S. Food and Drug Administration in the United States.

Financial regulation is a form of regulation or supervision, which subjects financial institutions to certain requirements, restrictions and guidelines, aiming to maintain the integrity of the financial system. This may be handled by either a government or non-government organization. Financial regulation has also influenced the structure of banking sectors, by decreasing borrowing costs and increasing the variety of financial products available.

The objectives of financial regulators are usually:

• market confidence – to maintain confidence in the financial system

• financial stability – contributing to the protection and enhancement of stability of the financial system

• consumer protection – securing the appropriate degree of protection for consumers.

• reduction of financial crime – reducing the extent to which it is possible for a regulated business to be used for a purpose connected with financial crime.

From Wikipedia, the free encyclopedia

## REP

A Retail Electric Provider (REP) sells electric energy to retail customers in the areas of Texas where the sale of electricity is open to retail competition. A REP buys wholesale electricity, delivery service, and related services, prices electricity for customers, and seeks customers to buy electricity at retail.

A REP has many responsibilities including:

• Buying electricity at wholesale.

• Buying delivery service and paying the charges for transmission and distribution service to the Transmission and Distribution Utilities TDU.

• Serving as the direct contact with the customer for electric service issues.

• Billing the customer and collecting for the REP's charges.

• Providing a 24-hour toll free telephone number for customer calls.

• Developing electronic interface system to communicate with the Independent System Operator (ERCOT) and other Market Participants relating to customer switches and meter information.

• Testing the electronic interface system with ERCOT.

• Understanding and following the Commission's rules, including customer protection rules.

From website of the Public Utility Commission of Texas, *https://www.puc.texas.gov*

## RTO

A regional transmission organization (RTO) in the United States is an organization that is responsible for moving electricity over large interstate areas. Like the European transmission system operator (TSO), an RTO coordinates, controls and monitors an electricity transmission grid.

An Independent System Operator (ISO) is an organization formed at the direction or recommendation of the Federal Energy Regulatory Commission (FERC). In the areas where an ISO is established, it coordinates, controls and monitors the operation of the electrical power system, usually within a single US State, but sometimes encompassing multiple states. RTOs typically perform the same functions as ISOs, but cover a larger geographic area.

RTOs were created by the Federal Energy Regulatory Commission (FERC) Order No. 2000, Issued on December 29, 1999. The four required characteristics are:

• Independence – the RTO must be independent of any market participant.

• Scope and regional configuration – the RTO must serve an appropriate region.

• Operational authority – the RTO must have operational authority for all transmission under its control.

• Short-term reliability – the RTO must have exclusive authority for maintaining the short-term reliability of the grid it operates

There are eight functions, including Tariff administration and design, Congestion management, Parallel path flow, Ancillary services, OASIS Total

Transmission Capability and Available Transmission Capability, Market monitoring, Planning and expansion, and Interregional coordination.

Only electric utilities that are located within the United States fall under FERC authority, but a larger organization called the North American Electric Reliability Corporation (NERC) overlays the entire FERC footprint and also includes a Mexican utility and several Canadian utilities. As such, international reciprocity is commonplace, and rules or recommendations introduced by FERC often are voluntarily accepted by NERC members outside of FERC's jurisdiction. Therefore, one Canadian Province is a member of a U.S.-based RTO, while two others function as an Electric System Operator (ESO), an organization essentially equal to a U.S.-based ISO.

Some ISOs and RTOs also act as a marketplace in wholesale power, especially since the electricity market deregulation of the late 1990s. Most are set up as nonprofit corporations using governance models developed by FERC.

From Wikipedia, the free encyclopedia

## Scalable

Scalability is the ability of a system, network, or process to handle a growing amount of work in a capable manner or its ability to be enlarged to accommodate that growth. For example, it can refer to the capability of a system to increase its total output under an increased load when resources (typically hardware) are added. An analogous meaning is implied when the word is used in an economic context, where scalability of a company implies that the underlying business model offers the potential for economic growth within the company.

Scalability, as a property of systems, is generally difficult to define and in any particular case it is necessary to define the specific requirements for scalability on those dimensions that are deemed important. It is a highly significant issue in electronics systems, databases, routers, and networking. A system whose performance improves after adding hardware, proportionally to the capacity added, is said to be a scalable system.

An algorithm, design, networking protocol, program, or other system is said to scale if it is suitably efficient and practical when applied to large situations (e.g. a large input data set, a large number of outputs or users, or a large number of participating nodes in the case of a distributed system). If the design or system fails when a quantity increases, it does not scale. In practice, if there are a large number of things (n) that affect scaling, then resource requirements (for example, algorithmic time-complexity) must grow less than n2 as n increases. An example is a search engine, that must scale not only for the number of users, but for the number of objects it indexes. Scalability refers to the ability of a site to increase in size as demand warrants.

## SGIP

The Smart Grid Interoperability Panel (SGIP) is a public/private funded, global, nonprofit organization that supports the work behind power grid modernization through the harmonization of technical interoperability standards to advance grid modernization. SGIP's stakeholders include utilities, manufacturers, consumers and regulators.

SGIP's mission is to accelerate the implementation of interoperable smart grid devices and systems.

SGIP fulfills its mission by coordinating and collaborating with stakeholders across the end-to-end Smart Grid enterprise. SGIP furthers Smart Grid interoperability by:

• Developing reference architectures and implementation guidelines;

• Facilitating and harmonizing standards development;

• Identifying testing, certification, and security requirements;

• Informing and educating stakeholders;

• Conducting outreach to establish global interoperability alignment.

From Wikipedia, the free encyclopedia

## Smart Meters

A smart meter is usually an electronic device that records consumption of electric energy in intervals of an hour or less and communicates that information at least daily back to the utility for monitoring and billing purposes. Smart meters enable two-way communication between the meter and the central system. Unlike home energy monitors, smart meters can gather data for remote reporting. Such an advanced metering infrastructure (AMI) differs from traditional automatic meter reading (AMR) in that it enables two-way communications with the meter.

From Wikipedia, the free encyclopedia

## Tariff

An electricity tariff is a schedule of fees or prices that relate to the receipt of electricity from a specific provider. Sometimes known simply as electricity pricing, the structuring of this type of schedule will vary from one country to another. In communities where there is more than one electricity provider authorized to offer commercial or residential services, there is also the chance that the exact price or tariff charged by each competing provider will vary slightly. Often, the price range for the electricity tariff is structured so that it complies with any local governmental agency charged with the oversight of utility pricing within that jurisdiction.

Source: Wisegeek *http://www.wisegeek.com/what-is-an-electricity-tariff.htm*

## TE (Transactive Energy)

Transactive Energy is business and regulatory model for electricity and business processes for this model.

## TE Platform

A TE Platform is an electronic service that records tenders and transactions among parties. Communication with parties is based on the TeMix Protocol.

## TE Platform Providers

A TE Platform Provider is an entity that hosts a TE Platform.

## TE System Interface

A TE Interface for a party uses the TeMix Protocol to communicate tenders and transactions with TE Platforms while typically hosting an Energy Management System that controls devices and systems owned by the party

## TeMix

TeMix (Transactive Energy Market Information) was defined by OASIS EMIX to refer the energy market information model to communicate simple energy and transport tenders and transactions.

## TeMix protocol

The TeMix Protocol is a defined profile of OASIS EI and OASIS EMIX. It is focused on automation of the transactive process for communicating tenders, transactions and delivery of energy and transport products.

## Tender

A binding bid or offer of money in payment for an energy transaction. A tender must specify and expiration date and time and all of the attributes of the proposed transaction.

## Transaction

An energy transaction is defined as an exchange among parties of an energy commodity for a payment.

## Transactive Energy Platform

A TE Platform is an electronic service that records tenders and transactions among parties. Communication with parties is based on the TeMix Protocol.

## Transport

Transport moves energy from one location to another.